CHILCOTIN
HOLIDAY

CHILCOTIN HOLIDAY

PAUL ST. PIERRE

Douglas & McIntyre
Vancouver/Toronto

Second printing, 1984
Douglas & McIntyre Ltd., 1615 Venables Street,
Vancouver, British Columbia V5L 2H1

Canadian Cataloguing in Publication Data

St. Pierre, Paul, 1923-
Chilcotin holiday

Originally published: Toronto: McClelland
and Stewart, 1970.
ISBN 0-88894-417-9
I. Title.
PS8537.A54C49 1984   C813'.54   C84-091078-9
PR9199.3.S24C49 1984

Cover photograph by Kris Andrews
Design by Barbara Hodgson
Printed and bound in Canada by D. W. Friesen & Sons Ltd.

Contents

Prologue

A man on a Chilcotin Holiday has one saddle horse, one rifle, one shaker of salt and nothing more. He knows not where he is going, whom he may meet, where he shall sleep, what he may eat or when he might return. He is untrammelled either by possessions or a sense of purpose. He is gloriously free. He may be off his head, of course, but that doesn't matter.

My years as a columnist on the *Vancouver Sun* had the quality of a Chilcotin Holiday. It was, in many ways, like being paid to take a continuous vacation. I cannot remember mentioning this to the publisher when matters of salary were under discussion. Probably it slipped my mind at the time. But it was true.

I had a fast and agile little riceburner, the first series of the Datsun 510s. It was designed and built so well as to be almost indestructible and it cornered on the mountain roads like a wet dishrag. A delight to drive. More than once I put a thousand miles on the clock in a day. When I ran dry of ideas in Vancouver, which was fairly often, I would wrap a pair of socks around a toothbrush and scoot away to the hills to hunt for somebody to write about. They were never hard to find. This world is loaded with interesting people who, because they happen to be obscure, are never picked up in the normal newspaper routine.

The newspaper columnist need only look for them and reflect in his words what they say. In this he enjoys a tremendous and quite unfair advantage over newspaper reporters. Newspaper reporters are the most important people in the entire industry. They are vastly more important than columnists or editors or publishers. But they are foot soldiers and are treated as foot soldiers usually are—misdirected and mistrusted by superiors who would not exist if reporters were not there.

One of the reporter's problems is that he finds himself obliged to report what any solemn and overpaid ass in authority may care to say. He must attend a press conference in the Pentagon or some other hive of bureaucracy and record statements which he knows, which all reasonable men know, to be patent nonsense. He is expected to do this with a straight face, solely for the reason that somebody with a title or a degree has said it. The columnist—some, at least, such as myself—is free of this frightful restriction. He has the immense privilege of ignoring the twits of our society, even when they occupy high places, as so many do. The columnist is allowed to write about real people instead.

The columns in this book cover the years 1965–1979. As the selection indicates, I found a very favourable ratio of real people, as opposed to twits, among residents of the Chilcotin Country. The Chilcotin has no monopoly on what I call real people. They are to be found everywhere, as I hope a few of the columns indicate. But Chilcotin was my old stamping ground. It was there I most often fled when I felt the need to touch the plain earth of reality and, at the same time, be reminded that the stuff of dreams is real in the life of everyone.

Whether in Chilcotin or elsewhere, I also was reminded of what it is so easy to forget in the corporate-bureaucratic society—the ordinary man has a great sense of fairness as well as common sense. Without doubt, some of the people of whom I wrote did not like what I said. But if the facts were moderately straight, they did not complain. And when I expressed opinions, even wrongheaded ones, they did not object if they could believe that they were honestly held opinions.

There are, of course, lies in here. I'm rather proud of some of them. But they will be accepted in the West and not noticed in the East, so everything works out for the best.

The land was beautiful. Most of what I saw was still under the proprietorship of God, and all the sunsets were free. Great years. Great people.

Why didn't I continue on a Chilcotin Holiday until I died? I don't know. I suppose no holiday lasts forever.

Doing the Impossible
for the Ungrateful

BIG CREEK—Beside the river called Big Creek is a thin road pointed toward the headwaters. The road becomes fainter with each ranch it passes and eventually it is lost in grassy meadows not far below the timberline.

That was the road on which I learned much about bulls, trucks, and Bruce Watt, and now I have a powerful respect for that piece of road and never go near it.

Bruce Watt was owner of the Breckness Ranch at Big Creek. He is a good rancher, although terribly afflicted with optimism.

Amid the varied equipment of the Breckness Ranch there stood an ancient one-ton Chev truck. Early one morning Bruce became seized with an ambition to fire up that truck and deliver one of his Hereford bulls to the high country where cows and heifers panted for want of his love. The bull's love.

"Come on along with us," Bruce said, "we'll only be gone a couple of hours."

Two hours later the coffee pot was empty and we finally left the ranch. There were four of us—Bruce, myself, Al Burnett, who then cowboyed for Bruce, and a one-ton Hereford bull of sullen temperament.

The bull had to be prodded vigorously before he would get in that truck. He was smarter than he looked.

The truck had been used fully by a logging outfit who offered to sell it to Bruce when they finished work in that area. Bruce didn't want to buy. Then they offered to give it to him. That offended him. He finally bought it for $25 and had driven it joyously for several years.

Sometimes he seemed to prefer it to other trucks on the ranch which were built after 1939.

His children, he said, had all learned to drive on this machine and that was good, because it had no brakes. "Any damn fool can drive something with brakes, but when you learn without brakes, then you become a driver," he said.

It also appeared to have no gas. The gauge read 0. We asked about this. Bruce said the gauge had never worked. He had filled the tank recently, he was sure. If he hadn't, no doubt one of the boys had. We drove on.

After a couple of hours in the rocks and the ruts the truck was boiling merrily. That did not bother Bruce. He does not worry easily. After a while, as he predicted, we came to Groundhog Creek, which is two inches deep and twenty-eight inches from shore to shore.

Using old oil cans and, if memory serves, somebody's hat, we filled the radiator.

Al pulled out the dip stick and said, "You are out of oil too."

"By golly, look at that, I am," said Bruce.

We found two full cans of oil in the cab and poured them in, hoping to quench a shudder in the engine's main bearing which had been noticeable for a few miles.

When Bruce fired up the engine the accelerator linkage separated into seventeen pieces and fell in seventeen places on the ground.

"We'll have to fix that," said Bruce. Al and I both agreed that we would have to fix it.

Bruce pulled out the seat and found beneath a nest made by field mice. The mice had used short pieces of binder twine in constructing their home. He began to cheerfully knot these pieces together to make a string long enough to tie up the accelerator linkage.

Al and I, having by now some measure of the man we were with that day, went to the back of the truck and tore off the tail light wires. After stripping the insulation we got enough copper wire to repair the accelerator.

The bull shifted his weight from time to time but made no other contribution to the festivities.

When Bruce had proceeded upriver for some three or more hours we began to suggest that he release the bull so that we could go home. He would not because, he said, unless there were cows in view the bull might become discouraged and walk home after us, having done nothing for the next generation of Herefords on the Breckness Ranch.

It began to rain. The truck boiled some more. Just beyond Fire Creek we got stuck in a broad, empty, nameless meadow. We jacked up the back in order to sling on tire chains. The jack broke.

We released that bull, cows or no cows, pointed him to the upper end of the meadow, kicked his ass, and told him to think of love. He went glumly away, giving us not one glance of thanks or compassion. Al and I both felt ours was the classic case of the unlucky doing the impossible for the ungrateful.

We had been almost seven hours away from the ranch when we got the truck free and turned homeward.

"By golly," said Bruce, "where has the day gone?"

We told him it had gone on his bloody truck.

He said she was a pretty good $25 truck, considering.

Surprising, wasn't it, how good you could manage with no windshield swipes and only one headlight. That was when the left front wheel fell off.

The front suspension was ball and socket joint. One socket had been eroded during the long greaseless years and now loosed its grip upon the ball joint. "We'll have to fix that," said Bruce.

We got the front of the truck up with a jack we knew to be good, for we had recently repaired it. "I think if I'm careful she will sort of balance there," said Bruce.

We made twenty feet before it fell out again. There were still twelve miles to go.

We jacked and perched the socket on the ball a second time. We made almost fifty feet before it fell out.

It rained harder.

It was at this time that Al said he was not, by nature, a man given to despondency but he didn't think the truck was going to get us home that night.

We walked through the mud to Sherwood Henry's and borrowed his pickup. We got back to the ranch at midnight.

That trip of a couple of hours had run to sixteen. If Bruce noted that a bit of extra time had been used up, he never mentioned it.

He tells me he went back and fixed that truck and she ran surprisingly well for a long time. Al works for the highways department now. I have no idea what the bull is doing. I don't care.

The Father of the Groom

WILLIAMS LAKE—A very successful wedding has just been held here. There was organ music, confetti, a bride and bridesmaids as fair as the dawn, and a big bowl of punch at the Elks Hall.

Weddings don't just happen. People have to plan them. Not enough of us appreciate this, and it is about time that some of us did. Consider, in this matter, the dressing of the Father of the Groom.

His name is Lester Dorsey. He has been ranching for forty-odd years in the Anahim Lake country. He has many horses. Many, many horses. In fact, many, many, many horses. Some of the LD brand are feeding almost as far east as Alexis Creek. He has many friends, even though he is an old rancher.

Although Pan Phillips held over at Quesnel, and some of the other Chilcotin men had to stay home to feed stock, a great many other friends of the Father of the Groom came to the wedding. They were earnestly intent on doing their bit to make it a success. It was decided by these friends that the Father of the Groom should wear a white shirt with a stiff collar. Also a necktie. The necktie, made of cloth, was purchased at Burkowski's store. It was coloured more or less like latigo, but was cheaper and softer. A Forsythe shirt was obtained at Mackenzie's store.

The dressing of the Father of the Groom took place in Room 218 of the Lakeview Hotel. Randolph Mulvahill of Chezacut helped to hold him down. The Father of the Groom had, by God, never worn a white shirt and tie in his life, and before he did, Hell would freeze solid from shore to shore. Even then, he said, he was prepared to sit around on the ice for a spell first.

Some furniture got overturned. A cowboy named George sat on his legs and Mike Dorsey, Brother of the Groom, also helped.

After Mr. Dorsey had been placed inside the boiled shirt, and the necktie had been cinched up tight against his Adam's apple, which is rather like an old pine-tree knot, his friend Mr. Mulvahill became sentimental about the whole business.

Mr. Mulvahill said that he had never realized that his friend L. Dorsey, Father of the Groom and holder of the LD horse brand, had such a natural elegance about him. Clearly, said Mr. Mulvahill, Mr. Dorsey had missed his calling. He should have been a stockbroker in Vancouver, or even Toronto.

Mr. Mulvahill spoke sadly of his own condition, that of a poor, simple Chilcotin rancher who still wore his pants inside his boot-tops. Here he was, he said, obliged to attend this wedding in an open-neck blue shirt and jeans.

Mr. Mulvahill offered to go away into a dark corner of the hotel and sit there all night, worrying about this. Mr. Dorsey said that Mr. Mulvahill could go right ahead and do that very thing.

Mr. Mulvahill then spoke with deep sincerity of the days when his friend Lester rode seventy-five miles across the mountains to the Mulvahill ranch, wearing an open-neck shirt and thin coat and scarcely anything more, surviving the most vicious winter weather by sheer strength of character. Times had changed, said Mr. Mulvahill.

The Father of the Groom was put into a suit. A white handkerchief was placed in the upper left front pocket. There was applause. The Father of the Groom was dusted, combed, and heavily advised.

Randolph Mulvahill wept, on behalf of himself, an ordinary rancher to whom the fused collar and the reversible cuff were unknown. He suggested that his good friend, the Father of the Groom, once an ordinary rancher like himself, should now slowly wean himself from that lowly estate. He suggested that Mr. Dorsey might next keep milk cows. From that he could go to sheep. He would then be ready to become an insurance salesman or bank manager or some other damn thing of that sort.

The Father of the Groom was escorted away from Room 218 and he went to the church and sat there quietly, thinking thoughts that are not known to us.

The Lakeview management plan to put up a small plaque over Room 218. Nothing gaudy. Just a small piece of bronze. It will say:

This is the Room
Where Lester Dorsey of the Anahim Country
Got into a White Shirt and Tie
For the First Time

With all this planning, the wedding was, of course, a success. The bride wore white.

When the wedding was over, Lester gave me back the shirt and tie. He said once was enough.

The management knew nothing of those events in Room 218 until they read my newspaper column some time later. To make an honest man of me, they had the bronze plaque made up and tacked it to the door. It was stolen and they put up another, and then another. But the plaques kept getting pinched so after a while they gave up and now there is hardly a guest who passes through that establishment who can tell where history was made.

Give Me a Small Town

Give me a small town that turns out the lights and sleeps at night.

I want a town too small to support a professional fire department. A volunteer brigade is good enough.

In the brigade there may be two companies. One company, of younger citizens, may be known as the Hackers and Bashers; the other, composed of their fathers and uncles, goes by the name Save The Outbuildings and The Rest Will Burn Itself Out.

When there is a fire, and that's seldom, the church bells ring and members of both companies run to the fire or, if it's very far, take their cars. Once at the scene they argue about how to attack this problem. The volunteer brigade's chief can't help because he is drunk. He is always drunk. He is the town drunk.

In this town, people are careful about fire.

There can be a few policemen in this town, but none who has been to a police academy or who has read books on criminology. They were appointed by the Town Council.

Being ordinary people like the rest of us, courts and lawyers frighten these policemen. They will do their utmost to keep disputes out of the courts so the citizens have to settle most things for themselves and have learned thereby to get along tolerably with one another.

I ask for a town with one mean man. He is very rich, for a town like this, but stingy, and neighbours say he heats the butter knives so his children can't smear too much butter on their bread.

Everybody waits for the day when the meanest man will be revealed to have a heart of gold. Some Christmas, perhaps, he will pull a drunken stranger out of a snowbank. Perhaps he will stealthily send the widow's son to McGill to become a famous surgeon.

He never does such things, but the possibility of his conversion remains to tantalize his fellow citizens.

In this town the most brilliant wit is the birthright of the local prostitute, and the financial genius of a John Paul Getty is possessed by the Public Works foreman who is known for nothing but his ability to hunt deer. The soul of a saint can be seen dimly behind the pale eyes of the man with a thirty-year-old body and an eight-year-old mind.

People in larger places may lament that talents are fearsomely wasted here, but this is not so. If a flower bloom and die on a mountain meadow, never seen by human eye, was it a wasted flower?

A town, pray, where the mayor has been returned by acclamation for twelve years, because nobody wants to hurt his feelings. He enjoys being mayor.

And where one of the main street merchants dresses up, once a month, in women's clothing, but nobody ever mentions it.

There should be a lot of small stores in this town and no big ones. The hardware store has a sign IN GOD WE TRUST, ALL OTHERS PAY CASH. The hardware gives credit surreptitiously. So do all the other merchants. It is considered dishonorable to run a store with no bad debts.

In this town is one doctor, who came there after some kind of trouble with the College of Physicians and Surgeons in the big city. The doctor is said to smoke opium and it is known that he is visited often at night by perfumed women who drive expensive cars.

It is generally agreed that he is a terrible character but everybody knows that had he chosen he could have become one of Canada's most famous surgeons. Because the people's faith in him is limitless their illnesses heal quickly, even if he does no more for them than talk in a soft voice and prescribe aspirin.

People in this town go home for lunch, which they call dinner.

The poor have names in this town. They are not figures written on pieces of paper but men, women, and children who are seen. No citizen can free himself of the knowledge that their lives are hard, nor can he exorcise his own daemon of greed merely by writing a cheque or paying his taxes.

It is a town that appreciates its heroes. There aren't many. One lady won a bronze medal in the Olympics, twenty-five years ago, and there is a First World War vet who won the Military Medal and Bar.

In the big and busy places these two people would be briefly acclaimed and soon forgotten but in little towns appreciation of great deeds lasts for a lifetime. One of the biggest projects undertaken in this town was keeping the one-time Olympic runner sober to meet the Queen. The old vet pays no municipal taxes—not by formal resolution of Council but by the clerk persistently losing his tax notices, year after year.

The town must have a resident radical. He is vicious in his criticisms of the town's established families, which is almost all the families. He is the only man who attends all the town council meetings and the only candidate who has never been elected. Although he is called Upright, Forthright, and Never Right, the town's radical is an essential element of the town's soul and there is some unuttered public uneasiness because he is not well, is getting old, and where can somebody be found to take his place when he is gone?

I want a town that turns out the lights and goes to sleep at night.

If such there be, show me and there will I fly and be at rest, for a little while, until the city calls me home again.

The Frontier Town

Writing on the eve of a trip to the Arctic a couple of questions arise, the first of which I could well do without.

The first question is, who has been stealing years away from me around this place? A trip to the North was always an annual or semiannual event. Overnight, three years went by. Not one, not two, but three full years since I have been up North. Who is taking those years from me and what did he do with them?

The other question may be answered in the course of the drive. Is there a frontier town left to be seen?

I fancy the answer is no.

Almost certainly, there is not a frontier town left in British Columbia. There may be one or two that can be reached by road in the Yukon or the Northwest Territories, but even this I doubt. The frontier town, too, has probably been stolen away by the silent years which have been drifting past.

There is plenty of frontier left in Canada and there are any number of towns built on the frontiers. The names come tumbling out—Yellowknife, Atlin, Mackenzie, Fort Nelson, Stewart, Hay River; there are dozens, scores, perhaps a hundred communities on the frontier.

But being on a frontier does not make a frontier town.

The Canadian custom of recent decades has been to change what frontier towns exist and to prevent new ones developing. We have chosen instead to package little bits of suburbia from settled Canada and plant them, complete, in the wilderness.

Even the newest of towns on frontiers are now born complete with many or most of the familiar amenities. There is pavement, a supermarket, day care centres, elected town councils, swimming pools which are heated, and bureaucrats which are not.

The frontier may lie at that town's edge, as moody, strange, savage, and enchanting as ever. Nevertheless it is possible for a man to move from a southern city, live several years within such a community's boundaries, and leave without ever having experienced anything radically different from what he might expect in Kelowna or in Trail.

The frontier town was profoundly different. It had a special and unique quality, which registered instantly and on all the senses.

That included the sense of smell. Frontier towns were usually dirty. Garbage disposal was left to dogs, bears, ravens, crows, foxes or whatever local collection agency nature might provide. Usually such creatures did a less than thorough job.

Another reason for dirt was the lack of pavement. Dust in summer and mud in spring were inescapable. No home was so poor that it lacked a front porch where you removed your boots before entering, but the dirt came in anyway. And the white, clean snows of winter in these towns quickly was soiled by black ash, by spilled oil, by the yellow pee of a multitude of quarrelsome dogs.

A frontier town seldom had streets with names and it never had them with house numbers. Being usually but a few hundred individuals, all of whom spent abundant spare time in discussing other individuals, everybody's home was known instinctively. No directions were needed to find it, day or night, any more than you require directions to walk through your own living room in darkness.

In addition to no garbage service there was also no mail delivery service, no regular bus, train or plane, and usually no resident doctor.

There was no such thing as a service industry in the town except for one bootlegger and sometimes one cafe.

The town grew utterly free of recognizable plan. Either because it had not been surveyed or because it had but people forgot where, houses went up any old place in any old style. Often they huddled close to one another, like caribou drawing into close ranks at the approach of wolves.

The building code was not known. A citizen might choose to build well and be comfortable. He might prefer to den up in some hole left by a bear. It was assumed that men and women had the wit to make choices such as these for themselves and although the view may seem quaint to the modern urban resident, to frontier town people it is just as curious for people to depend upon government to tell them how they should be housed.

Nor were health regulations known.

If one chose to build the outdoor privy next to the well there could be but two results, and both were good. The citizen would accumulate antibodies in his bloodstream which would enable him to safely partake of hospitality in the homes of others with similar sanitary facilities.

Failing this he could die of typhoid, as nature had obviously intended for him, thus relieving neighbours of responsibility for a person unsuited to the frontier world.

The respect for old-timers, sometimes called pioneers, was universal in frontier towns.

Old-timers were never treated as incompetents or as cranks, even if they were. They were not asked to change their ways, either for their own sakes or anyone else's. Their independence, which most kept until the day no smoke arose from their chimney, was respected.

By the act of survival on the frontier, these people had paid their dues. In old age they might be saintly or satanic. That didn't matter. They were freemen of the town.

A frontier town usually had but one policeman and he stayed a long time. Citizens would even protest the transfer of an unpopular policeman. They might not like the man, but they knew him.

As for the policeman, it was his job to let everybody know, in ways that they would understand, which laws of Canada he intended to enforce and which ones he held to be a bunch of nonsense.

There was almost always a missionary in the town and he, too, often made similar selective judgements in applying the teachings and practices of his church.

Dozens of other particular features of the frontier town could be listed by anyone who lived in one or visited one often. They were particular places in this country. Indeed, throughout our history, these were the outposts on which we built most of our modern cities and towns.

If the last of them are now gone, or so thoroughly disinfected as to be unrecognizable, I shall not be surprised. Sad, perhaps, but not surprised.

Everything You Need to Make a Ranch

ALEXIS CREEK—We were in a ranch-house kitchen the other night hunting for the bottom of a whisky bottle when the question came up of what you need to be a rancher today.

Health and brains we didn't count. It's never been proven the first is necessary and the second can actually be a handicap.

We threw out stamina, endurance, and ambition, too. Those are just brag subjects.

As for expanded knowledge of new ranching techniques, the hell with them. Most ranchers in Chilcotin aren't running their places as well as they already know how to.

Love of cows and horses didn't count. There wasn't a rancher present who would admit to anything more than a bare tolerance of either.

We decided it was time to be practical, to discuss the priorities, the way the prime minister advises us.

These emerged as the priorities for ranching today, listed in the order of their importance.

The first thing to get was a pickup truck. Fact is, it's getting hard to remember if there were ranchers before there were pickups.

The pickup should have power brakes and power steering, a deer-gun rack behind the seat, and Farm Vehicle written on the side. In the box there should be a broken jack, a bale of hay, and a dog. Almost any dog that barks will do.

The next important thing is an accountant, preferably a smart one.

This accountant's job is to understand most of the federal and provincial government regulations. He should be tested occasionally.

If the accountant interprets regulations correctly just 50 per cent of the time, he is only guessing and you could do as well yourself. Find one that can read the regulations right at least two times out of three.

You will need a good tax lawyer, too. He will explain why heavy losses are your only hope. That will fit right in with what you're doing. Give him a piece of the ranch from time to time.

You will need to know all you can about feed grain subsidies and the Crow's Nest Pass freight rates. Study them for a few years. If you get good at them, you can quit ranching and become chairman of the Canadian Transport Commission, which is indoor work with no heavy lifting.

A good banker is next.

Find one who doesn't understand anything about ranching. That won't be hard.

It would be best if you don't know anything about finance and cannot tell a demand note for 9½ per cent from a Rinso soap coupon. That way you and your banker will start out even, which is only fair. You can grow up together.

You will need a wife.

Find an attractive, intelligent, well-educated girl who likes carrying water in a pail and is happy to get laundry soap for a birthday present.

Raise a lot of kids. You will need the baby bonus to fix the pickup when they are young and you will find work for them to do from about the age of eight.

You will find the boys will work all right, up to the time they are old enough to pull the pin and head for Vancouver.

To keep the daughters cheerful, however, you will have to buy them at least one horse apiece, which they will spoil with love and cube sugar.

While you're at it, pick up some horses for yourself. They're not as handy as a plane or a motorcycle, but they sort of dress up the place.

Knowing your own ranch isn't enough; don't let yourself get cut off from the doings of the outside world. Buy a subscription to *Western Horseman*.

You will also need:

eighty-dollar boots;

a nickel-plated belt buckle;
some rope;
a set of moose horns for the living room wall, and
a cheque book.

Once you have put this all together you might try getting a cow and a bull together and see if anything happens.

You Want a Bridge?
Then Build a Bridge

ALEXIS CREEK—The Chilcotin, one of the larger and wilder rivers of this province, is now spanned a few miles east of here by a brand-new suspension bridge that was built so a six-year-old boy could get to school.

It is a spectacular sight, swooping down from a high cut bank on the river's northern shore, crossing 280 feet of rustling blue-green water, hanging at the southern shore on a 35-foot A-frame of peeled poles, and then plunging into the earth.

Spectacular it may be, but unspectacularly was it done. Nobody up here talks about it much. If you want a bridge, you build a bridge, don't you? Well, the Plummer family needed a bridge.

Wayne and Trina Plummer operate Neil Harvey's Deer Creek Ranch on the south side of the Chilcotin, halfway between the Chilco Ranch home place and the Duke Martin bridge near Alexis Creek.

They have two children, and as the oldest, Levi, neared his sixth birthday, they began to discuss how they would get him to the school bus on the Chilcotin Highway.

There is a road to the Deer Creek place and they could drive each morning and afternoon to the school bus stop—but this would be thirty-six miles a day and the road crosses an alkali flat that becomes an impassable bog many times each year. Sometimes they must keep vehicles on both sides of the bog hole, leaving one and walking across to pick up the other.

It seemed simpler to bridge the Chilcotin. That way it would only be necessary to build half a mile of road from the ranch house to the river bank and another eight-tenths of a mile through Dan Lee's ranch to the main highway.

Jack Casselman, a rancher noted for his handiness, had just sold his Brittany Lake Ranch and had some time to spare. The idea appealed to him. He had never built a suspension bridge before.

The other bridge builder was Wayne Plummer's brother-in-law, Lynn Bonner, of Riske Creek, who is the general manager of three ranches owned by Harvey in this area. He, too, was strongly attracted to the notion.

The bridge is called the Cassel-Lynn to honour these two entrepreneurs, but on the day I visited, Wayne Plummer was at the bridge, a hammer in his hand and a one-quarter-inch hand-rolled cigarette butt smouldering at his narrow lips.

"Jack Casselman did most of the work," he said. "He went down to Vancouver and looked at some bridges there. He said there didn't seem to be much of a trick to it. It took him about two-and-a-half months."

First, he pointed out, they bulldozed holes in the river bank and embedded concrete anchors, blocks twelve by eight by six feet.

They snaked one-inch cables across the river, slung them on the A-frame on the southern shore, and Jack began hanging straps and laying planks. He just began at one side and ended at the other side, that's all.

(Wayne is not a talkative man. What conversation he had to spare that morning he spent mostly on the price of beef, which he summed up finally in the short philosophic comment, "What the hell, somebody's got to be poor.")

The details of the bridge, as elicited that morning, are that the main cables are one inch thick and capable of holding fifty tons, the drop cables are five-sixteenths steel and good for five or ten tons apiece, the crosspieces for the walkway are Douglas fir three-by-fours and the planking, one-inch pine boards.

It had, he agreed, cost Neil Harvey a lot of money. For materials and for Jack Casselman's time, he had spent $8,000. This, by a quick calculation, amounts to between one-twentieth and one-thirtieth of the cost if it had been a government project; but it wasn't. Even if the government had helped, the price would have shot up. Everybody knows that.

Trina takes the little boy across each morning and afternoon on the back of a motorcycle. When the wind blows hard down the Chilcotin valley, the bridge has both a ripple and a whip, she reported, and the fun goes out of cycling.

So they have obtained a brave old Volkswagen Beetle.

Wayne is now engaged in running vertical planks on the sides of the four-foot bridge deck as a safety measure.

The Volkswagen will still be too wide for the bridge but he calculates that he can haul out the welding torch, cut three inches off the fenders and running board of the car, and make a neat fit of it.

Trina and Levi will be grateful when the wind blows, the snows come, or when, as occasionally happens, the temperatures hit forty below.

Yes, they had a bit of a party when the bridge opened. Even broke a champagne bottle over it, after first removing the contents, which should not be wasted. But after all, it's just a bridge to get Levi to school, and was there any reason to write it up in the newspaper?

God Seeks Permission

The application of Supreme Enterprises, proposing the creation of Heaven and Earth, is not likely to get approval in less than seven years. It meets few of the current criteria.

In the prospectus it is noted that earth is without form and void and that darkness is upon the face of the deep. It is proposed to change this.

Little thought seems to have been given to the political difficulties inherent in any attempt to alter or interfere with the void.

Environmentalists have suspected for a long time that powerful interests have designs upon the void. The Supreme Enterprises proposal will be seen as confirming this.

One prominent environmental consultant has promised that his group will take the issue to the Supreme Court of Canada.

"The void," he said, "is a priceless natural asset which we hold in trust for generations yet unborn. If lost, it would be irreplaceable." He said not much is known about void cycles. Until more is known, the void should be left untouched.

It is also noted that Supreme Enterprises proposes the creation of light immediately on starting operations. The Public Utilities Commission will have something to say about that.

No consideration can begin, said one commission member, until a rate structure has been put forward. Even then, considerable time for study will be necessary. Also the commission has a responsibility to consider the socioeconomic effect of light upon the licencee already established (darkness). "For the moment, we take it that the idea of creating light is more a general hope than a specific plan."

In the third phase of Supreme Enterprise operations, referred to in the prospectus as Third Day, it is proposed that the waters of earth be gathered into one place and that dry land appear.

Gathering the waters into one place can not be done except by specific permission of the Water Rights Branch in Victoria.

As for the dry land operation, the first reaction of the B.C. Land Commission was negative. "We are not told whether this is to be First, Second or Sixth Class Agricultural," said a spokesman. "The whole thing is deplorably vague."

It has been suggested that the Water Rights Branch and the Land Commission might give a temporary permit for Third Day but only on condition that the applicant agree to let the waters ungather and the dry land disappear on completion of the project.

Quoting further from the prospectus:

"Let the earth bring forth grass, the herb yielding seed, and the fruit tree yielding fruit after his kind, whose seed is in itself, upon the earth . . ."

This, of course, is dependent on the dry land phase being approved. However it will also involve the Forestry Department (grass), the Fruit Marketing Board (fruit tree yielding), and the RCMP drug squad (grass). Any one might veto the project.

"Let the waters bring forth abundantly the moving creature that hath life and fowl that may fly above the earth in the open firmament of Heaven."

There is a lot more to this than a bit of eelgrass and a few sparrows. At a first quick reading it can be seen to involve the federal Fisheries Department, the provincial Wildlife Department, the Marine Biological Station at Nanaimo, and all the Okanagan milfoil people.

As for free-flying fowl, if they are going to use the firmament of Heaven they will first require licences issued by the Ministry of Transport, whose firmament that is.

These are only a few of the agencies from whom clearance must be obtained. Building a brick outhouse in the Cariboo now requires the approval of eight different agencies, and Supreme Enterprises clearly envisages work of a more imposing nature.

Phase Sixth Day is similarly fraught with difficulties.

"Let the earth bring forth the living creature after his kind, cattle and creeping thing and beast of the earth . . ."

The application ignores the limited carrying capacity of Crown grazing range. No reason is offered for the introduction of creeping things. What are they to be and will they enhance the environment? What kind of beasts are proposed? Is the English starling included?

The general objectives of Supreme Enterprises are stated in Section 28, but in terms so terse, so general of application, that they are unlikely to withstand any departmental scrutiny.

"Be fruitful, and multiply, and replenish the earth and subdue it; and have dominion over the fish of the sea and over the fowl of the air and over every living thing that moveth upon the earth."

Vague as it is, brief as it is, unsatisfactory as it is, the serious socioeconomic problems it suggests are plain enough.

While to be fruitful is not necessarily objectionable, there should be some documentation by Supreme Enterprises of anticipated market conditions; it is against public policy to encourage enterprises which may not prove economically viable.

Subdue the earth? The United Nations charter is specific on that point, and we are signatory to the charter.

Dominion? Why dominion? May it not also be provincial and municipal in scope?

As for controlling every living thing that moveth on earth, that is already being done by government agencies long established.

The least controversial element of the prospectus is the final section—on the Seventh Day Supreme Enterprises proposes to rest.

This seems in accordance with the Lord's Day Act. However, Vancouver City Council has not yet rendered a final decision on observance of the Sabbath so this, too, cannot be approved at this time.

Man, Dog and Mystery

The man and the dog began working the pheasant cover below the orchard at 8 A.M., strangers to one another and with traces of the hostilities and contempts that go with master-and-slave relationships.

The dog was a springer spaniel of the North American strain—smaller than the English forebears of the breed, dainty, prettily marked, and probably brainless. The man had borrowed it and spent a fortnight trying to get it to come when called and keep off the bloody furniture.

It was abjectly nervous and quivered at a harsh word. If the man whacked its rump for misbehaving it sometimes wet itself. The owners must have punished it as a pup for wetting on the carpet, and although he knew they used nothing but a folded newspaper, the dog's dim brain had not sorted out cause and effect.

The pheasant cover was a five-acre patch of rank grasses, tules, cockleburrs, vetch, bramble, and thistle lying below an apple orchard. All those weeds that men despise and pheasants love were there deserving, the man thought, of something far better than this gutless wonder to hunt in them.

The miracle, and no other word came to the man's mind, occurred within ten minutes when the little springer, after a few dubious glances over its shoulder, began to sweep the ground for birds.

It flashed over the frost diamonds in the grass and thrashed through hardhack with its stub-tail quivering. It took scent from the cold ground and paused from time to time to throw up that handsome head for air scent.

The man watched with a growing interest and offered some encouragement, saying, "Hunt 'em out," and, "Birds, boy, birds," and his heart moved a few extra beats when he saw the liver-and-white patched body of the dog go into rapid changes of stride in heavy cover. Then the dog began to spring and the man's breath stopped, for there are few such sights.

The dog's body bounded two feet above the weeds, four little legs wide to the winds, the long ears flying loose and high. One, two, three great springs and he busted the bird that had thought to hide from him, and everything—the great clattering cock pheasant, the bounding dog, the sound of the gun, sky, the smell of the morning—everything that was radiant perfection became encapsuled in one tiny instant.

The dog bit much too hard into the pheasant's body when he picked it up, but thoughts about soft mouth and pretty deliveries were for another time. It was his first bird.

The man let him snuffle in the pheasant's feathers, rub his ears on the bird's body, even snatch a couple of long tail feathers in his teeth. Where had all this blazing fire come from?

They hunted for their legal eight hours that day, and the more the man saw the less he understood.

He knew something of why the dog chose to work for him. Descended, like all domestic dogs, from prototypes of the wolf and the jackal families, his instinct was to accept a leader. A human substituted easily for an older, wiser boss dog of a pack.

But how did a fourteen-month-old lap dog—for such this dog was in his owner's home—know so much, so quickly, without training and without command?

Wherever they moved the dog coursed, left and right, always in the direction in which the man walked. It was always a set distance, close in heavy cover, far when they walked the cropped grass under the trees of the orchard. Whenever the man switched the direction of his walk, so did the dog.

He observed that the dog frequently looked back over his shoulder to check where the man was moving, but once, as an experiment, the man said to himself, "I am going to make a right-angle turn after three more steps" and before the steps were complete the dog had swung right so that it ranged before him on the new course. Pure coincidence, of course.

The man did not believe that telepathy existed among humans and he was certainly not prepared to believe it bridged species of animals.

One should not inject too much magic into an ordinary hunt,

and the dog didn't really look reproachfully at him when he failed to shoot at hen pheasants, did it?

The man thought about the hen pheasant and the gap that must always exist between him and his animal hunting partner. By various devices, he could teach this dog dozens of tricks. He could teach it to respond to the question, "What's going to happen to the government in the next election?" by lying down and turning over. But he could never communicate any sense of legal and illegal birds. The dog would have to accept some actions of the man as forever inexplicable.

So, come to think of it, must he accept some decisions of the dog that would be forever beyond his understanding.

Why did the dog accept a signal to hunt in thorns and thistles and evade an order to work a likely-looking patch of vetch. It made sense, the man decided, to give the dog the dignity of making some decisions himself.

They did not hunt in the same world. The man saw blue sky, red apples on the trees, and rich irridescence in the pheasants' feathers. The dog saw only a dim world of grey, hazy shades and, if human, would be categorized as almost blind.

In scent, the dog could not only follow the invisible path of a running bird through grass but it also could tell, with scarcely a false step, in which direction the bird had run minutes before.

They must, the man knew, settle for what they did well and enjoyed together.

On the first day, when he was tired of carrying a bird in his hand, the man cached it in a bough of an orchard tree and picked it up later on his return to the car. Next morning, eighteen hours later, when the dog was let out of the car, it ran to the tree, second row, fifth from the end and stood on its hind legs to carefully check the branch where the bird had been wedged.

Their relationship was easier the second day, and the man did not spend himself in extravagant praise when the first bird was shot.

"Tonight," he told the dog, "I am not going to spend two hours pulling burrs out of your ears. I am going to take an axe and cut your ears off right next to your skull and solve the whole problem." The dog pressed his head under the man's hand for a caress and allowed as how that would be all right with him.

Burrs matted his ears again early in this second day. In one ear, where burr clung to burr, the flap was rolled into a tube like a Swiss pancake. There was blood on one foot from a thorn cut. His little scrotum shone cherry red between his legs—he was too short to clear the thorn bush as he coursed it for pheasant scent.

His ribs showed. He had to be coaxed to eat and then ate little. When away from the field, he collapsed into a sleep like death and could be lifted an inch or two and dropped to the floor without waking. He was, like the human hunter, dirty, tired, and happy to distraction.

When older, he could never maintain a pace such as this for two days, but nature in her wisdom would compensate him. He would have acquired more bird sense and with less running would find just as many pheasants and handle them more easily.

"After a while," the man told him, "you will begin losing both muscles and brains and become an old fool, like me. But by then those around us will have become fond of us, for some perverse reason, and they will give us a certain amount of respect and even honour, worthless as we may be." He would have liked to have this dog grow old with him.

The two days had taught the dog many things but had taught the man more. The man had been privileged to be reminded of how little he knew about anything. His forefinger had touched, however briefly, the edge of nature's infinite mystery. His heart had been warmed by the friendship of another and different living creature.

Ollie Nikolaye,
Who Was Loved

ANAHIM LAKE—He was born Johnnie Robertson, his Indian name was *Nookelow*, and by some process of change that would be difficult to trace, he spent his life under the name Ollie Nikolaye.

By any standards, including the rather hard standards of the frontier, Ollie was given a poor start in life. His mother was an Indian and his father a white. His father died of gunshot in the Nmiah Valley, just about the time that the boy was born. His mother struggled along with the child for a few years. But when he was about ten, she gave him away to an Indian named Little Johnnie, a cowboy of the Tatla Lake Ranch.

Little Johnnie did his best for Ollie. For clothing, he bought him a suit of men's overalls, full size. The legs had to be cut off almost at the crotch to let the child's feet reach the ground, and the overalls were so big around the waist that they almost made a complete double-wrap when cinched up with a large belt. All cowboys agreed that little Ollie was about the most comical looking kid that the country could provide.

Little Johnnie was killed near Pinto Lake when thrown from his horse during the fall roundup. The other cowboys shot the offending horse and packed Little Johnnie back to the ranch on a packhorse.

There was an element of coincidence in the death of Little Johnnie. Pinto Lake is today one of the favourite haunts of Ollie's half-sister, who is nicknamed *Chee Wit* (The Chickadee). She lives in the bush most of the time—as wild, almost, as the deer. But this was all to come much later.

That autumn day, Ollie's childhood came to an official end. The only father he ever knew was dead, and it was time for him to work for his living. He lived for a time with Old Sulin at Morrison Meadow near here, then at the Three Circle Ranch, then at many other ranches. Ollie did not turn to rape, arson, and pillage, as is supposed to be common among people of such a deprived childhood. Instead, he developed all those qualities which are most highly prized in the cattle country.

He had immense endurance. His word was good. He loved adventure. He could work hard and play hard. He could fight, and over the years accumulated a gunshot wound and a knife scar.

He was a witty man, and could tell a better story in broken English than many a fluent man. The stories lose something in cold print, but some of the man's flair shows even in this fragment:

"When we come out of them jack pine, that grizzly bear ain't at that moose carcass any more. He has come around behind us and he is standing up on his hind legs behind that American. I say to that American, I say, 'I think you turn 'round, you see that bear he's close enough for pictures now.'

"Me, I put my gun on that bear's head. I say, 'I think you should hurry up them pictures.' But the American don't say nothing. I don't know what he's doing. I got no looks to give to that American, I got all my looks for that grizzly bear. Sure funny thing, that bear. He's got his mouth open, just like he's laughin' about something. I keep telling that man better he take them pictures fast, but he don't answer.

"After a little time, that bear goes away and then I look for that hunter. Funny thing, he ain't there at all. He is running. He is almost all the way back up the hill to that camp we got. All that time, I been just talkin' to myself."

Ollie married twice and had children. He never acquired his own ranch, nor did he ever learn to read or write. But luck was good enough to him. When he lost his saddle in a poker game, he could be expected to win it back with a set of chaps in addition at the next game. One year, he lost his trap line in a horse-shoe-pitching contest, but won it back the following year. Win or lose, his high good humour never changed.

Finally, in 1960, his luck ran out. He was setting choker on a logging show in the Bella Coola valley. The radio whistles were then just being introduced and something went wrong with one. A log crushed the life out of him.

He is buried at the Anahim Lake Indian Reserve cemetery, where some of the graves have little houses built over them. His tombstone is of granite. It says: "Ollie Nikolaye, 1906–1960, Died in Bella Coola. Rest in Peace."

The measure of the man, however, is not his rather expensive and formal grave marker, but in the powerful memories he has left in this region. Scarcely a man does not have a story to tell about the great Ollie Nikolaye, and all of these stories are told with respect and affection. His death is still deplored as a sinful waste. The death of kings has been forgotten in far less time here.

Incident at
Duke Martin Bridge

The Downwind Tracker is wintering well in Chilcotin, but there are always interruptions in the even tenor of ranch life. One of his most recent is an episode that will be known in the folklore of that band as The Incident at Duke Martin Bridge.

One of the neighbours reports as follows:

"The Downwind Tracker left the ranch in God's hands the other day and drove off to Alexis Creek with his wife to buy some kerosene or drink some beer or argue with the forestry people or do something else that advances the beef industry in B.C.

"There was an ice jam on the Chilcotin River and some water had flooded the approaches, but he made it all right in his Volkswagen. The Downwind Tracker drives a Volkswagen now, and everybody agrees it is a good thing for him—this is one winter where the old, old problem of remembering to put his antifreeze in soon enough does not exist for him.

"In Alexis Creek he did whatever he had in mind for strengthening this province's economy, and they started back across the river toward the Chilco ranch about sunset, across the Duke Martin Bridge.

"It was about twelve below White Man's. (I guess you know that nobody in Chilcotin has accepted Celsius, but we are not so much out of touch with the rest of the world that we don't know about it, so, to make things clear, we deal in Fahrenheit and call it White Man's Temperature.)

"His wife said she thought the water at the bridge approach looked deeper, but the Downwind Tracker said no, it wasn't any deeper; if anything, it was shallower. He has never found a cure for optimism.

"When he spurred the Volkswagen it lost traction pretty soon. That was because the wheels weren't touching the ground. It was floating.

"He has one of the old style Volkswagens which float. However, they also have a gas heater which vents to the outside and the river started running into the car through that hole.

"His wife pointed this out to him just about the time the motor stalled. When he opened the door the Chilcotin really began running into the car. She perched as high as she could on the seat and he got out and found himself up to his high pockets in ice water.

"He waded ashore, leaving her and the river there together in the car, and by luck somebody came by soon after in a truck.

"They got a cable on the Volkswagen and towed it back to shore. When he opened the door to collect his wife, the water all ran out and started down to rejoin the river. Her shoes floated out with the stream and they looked so funny that, although she had been a bit irritated with the old Tracker, she couldn't help laughing at the sight.

"Personally I think the Downwind Tracker is lucky to have married a woman with a sense of humour.

"They got the Volkswagen back to Alexis Creek where they got a room at the hotel. Next day, the car was dried out enough to start. Everything except the heater, that is.

"However the seats were all froze hard as planks and the doors wouldn't open. They had to go in and out through the windows, so they took it to the queer shop at Williams Lake.

"It took four days to dry out the Volkswagen and another day for the Downwind Tracker. I haven't found out what his errand was at Alexis Creek but I suppose it doesn't matter."

Cog Harrington

BOSTON BAR—How Sister Clara of Holy Rosary Cathedral almost but not quite provided free beer for Boston Bar is only a part of Cog Harrington's story.

It is a long story, aquiver with thrills and suspense, strung together with mystery and, from the heart, the thin keening of melancholy. Of course he always talks that way, but this time it is different.

Through shimmering heat waves flung off the blistering walls of the Fraser Canyon he is seen standing on the front lawn of the Charles Hotel, a beerless and unhappy man who has lost his identity.

A few days ago, he reports, he passed the magic mark of his 65th birthday. All should have been joy and gladness; all is bloody well not.

"Got two cheques. Canada Pension cheque for $194, old-age pension cheque for $165. Three hundred and fifty-nine dollars, all to spend buying free beer for Boston Bar, which is the way people are supposed to spend old-age pension cheques.

"Instead we get a goddam beer strike. The country might as well be Communist."

We go into the beer parlor, which is air-conditioned and entirely free of all trace of the hops. The beer parlor has just been renovated for $232,000, which shows you something about the state of the nation. Thirty years ago Cog built the whole hotel for $85,000.

Bracing himself to recount his deeper troubles, the truly desperate straits in which he finds himself while entering what was supposed to be carefree old age, The Cog offers to spring for what he calls a Cooler.

"What is a Cooler?"

"It's what you sell when you don't have beer. Pepsi-Cola in a beer glass, some ice and a bunch of wine. Any old kind of wine."

"Thanks just the same, I'll have ginger ale."

"If you're going to be reckless I'll be reckless too." He shouts across the new $11,000 carpet: "TONY, WE'RE GOING TO TAKE A CRACK AT GINGER ALE!"

Half a dozen loggers, seated glumly next to glasses filled with stuff the colour of dried blood, look over to observe the further decay of all the old values of Canada on this, the nation's 111th birthday.

The Old Cog peers into his ginger ale glass to check for piranhas and then sips some.

"Beer is the working man's drink," he said. "We have customers here come in at 11 o'clock in the morning, and 11 o'clock at night they're still here."

"Then they can't be working much."

"Sure they're working. They're working at drinking beer."

The beer parlor, he says, was selling about $2,500 worth of beer a day until the strike. Now it is selling about $800 worth of plonk.

Meanwhile his two pension cheques sit in the safe, uncashed, waiting for the day when the brewery workers will permit him to spend the money prudently.

Is that, then, his only trouble?

That is not half the damn trouble.

To get the old-age pension cheque he had to prove that he had been born. True enough, that event had occurred. But it happened across the river in North Bend which, in 1913, offered no facilities for registering births.

"I knew I'd been baptized at Holy Rosary in Vancouver, so I asked for my baptismal certificate. There was no baptismal certificate there for me."

He sighed. His glass was dry. Recklessly, he ordered us another round of ginger ales.

"I went to see Sister Clara and we went over the records. Then she found it.

"Do you know who I am?

"I am not Walter Harrington. My mother thought I was, my father thought I was, all my friends and bankers thought I was. Personally, I was totally convinced of it for 65 years. But it is not my name."

"What is your name?"

He let his plump body list closer and muttered it. "William Henry Michael Harrington. That's who I am. William Henry Michael.

"Now everybody around here is calling me Willie. 'Willie,' they say, 'where is the free birthday beer, Willie?' "

"What about your passport? What about all the legal documents you've been signing for half a century?"

His eye opened wide. (It is the last eye he has left.) "Hell's bells, I never even THOUGHT about that yet."

We take our leave of a thirsty, thwarted man who has lost his identity. Old Cog, Walter, William, Henry, Michael, Willie Harrington. In the hot, still air of the canyon the faint whimper of his voice floats: "Beer, dammit, is the working man's drink."

The Las Vegas Crabber

TOFINO—Bill White is an enterprising fellow who fishes crab in the open ocean near here from a custom-built Nova Scotia lobster boat. He sends the crabs to Los Angeles and Las Vegas and his money to the bank. It is hard and sometimes dangerous work, and it has produced a true son of the sea, a man of calm temperament, steady eye, clear voice, and unimpeachable integrity—as the following story will show.

One day, shortly before the 1961 season opened, Bill was tinkering with his boat when a large female approached on the float. "What are you doing?" she asked, being a tourist and as inquisitive as a puppy in a strange living room.

Bill answered in his simple, forthright way, explaining many of the intricacies of engine tune-up. He gave his answers immediately and fully. One might think that he had been paid to dispense information to tourists and was earnestly concerned lest he fail to give conscientious effort for money received.

Another boat was preparing for sea next to Bill's. "What," asked the tourist, "is that man doing?" Bill answered in his same honest, frank manner. "He's getting ready for fishing, too. Poor John, he's never going to make it."

"Oh?"

"A sad case," said Bill. "Every year, he spends all the money he's saved up to get the boat ready for fishing. And every year, just on the eve of the season, he gets blind drunk and stays drunk until all the best fishing is over."

The lady tourist looked at John. He certainly did seem to be working quite hard at getting the *Lucky Kid* ready for sea. John happened to glance up while she was looking at him. Then he returned to his work.

"How many fishing seasons has he missed?" asked the tourist.

"Seventeen," said Bill White. "Every season for seventeen years, he almost makes it to opening, and then some friends come around—and, bango, he's flat on his back."

John strolled over to borrow a ratchet. "You're looking twitchy today," remarked Bill, as he handed over the wrench.

This seemed to John a rather peculiar remark. But, being too busy for conversation, he did not answer and returned to his own boat with the wrench. As he climbed into his own boat, he looked back once more and noticed both Bill and the stranger looking at him with a peculiar expression.

"That's always the start," said Bill. "When he becomes silent." The lady walked over to look at John more closely. John looked at her, again interrupting his work. There was no conversation. The lady returned to Bill's boat.

"Is there no Alcoholics Anonymous here?" she said.

"We have tried to organize the alcoholics in this town, but they just will not organize. They are the most disorganized people you can imagine." The lady departed, thoughtfully.

When John returned the wrench he asked, "Who was that woman?"

"Just a visitor," said Bill.

"Did you notice how she looked at me?"

"I guess she's just interested in finding out what fishermen look like."

"I don't know. It was a funny kind of a look."

The hour was late and the wind chill, and Bill suggested that they repair themselves to the hotel for a glass of beer before dinner. John was not particularly interested. He is a hard-working and highly skilled fisherman and has no more than ordinary interest in drinking. However, he agreed to join Bill for a couple. After they were settled at their table, he asked: "Didn't you notice that woman again in the lobby, when we came through?"

"What woman?"

"The woman you were talking to down on the dock."

"Never noticed her," said Bill.

"She was giving you a funny look this time. A really funny look."

"She was?"

"She stared at you as though you were a tiger or something. What's the matter with that woman?"

"Who knows," said Bill. "I can never understand tourists myself. They're such complex people."

Bill White later became skipper of a Coast Guard vessel in those wild and dangerous waters. Even in the government service, he never ceased to view life with a remarkable sense of proportion.

"What happens to you, Bill, if you pile Her Majesty's ship up on the shore some day?" I said to him once.

"Oh, nothing," he said, "absolutely nothing. That doesn't matter. You just have to be sure to write reports about it later."

It Pays Better than Working

LILLOOET—Noel Baker, Lilloet's wheeler-dealer extraordinary, had risen early this day, but when the radio brought reports of the coming recession, he went back to bed.

As he often does, he lay there thinking, sometimes sleeping a bit, under the velvet painting of the naked girl that is reflected in ruby mirror glass on the ceiling. He was found there in early afternoon during one of the sleep periods.

"The way the presidents and the prime ministers are talking, I may have to go back to work," said Noel.

"You know, my Uncle Joe called the other day. 'Noel', he said to me, 'you spend half the year in Hawaii, you have an estate on the lakeshore, power boats, and all that fun, and yet somehow I never get to see you turning a wheel. Do you have an oil well I don't know about? Tell me how you do it and I will write a book about it and I'll get rich.' "

Many people in Lillooet have the same wonderment about Noel Baker. True, he trades in land and houses, and that has made many fortunes in B.C. But the other people don't do it in Lillooet, which has had a depression most of the time since the gold rush of the 1860s.

At present the town seems to be catching up to the general prosperity level of this province, but five years ago it had an unemployment rate of 75 per cent, which compares, unfavourably, with that in some Newfoundland outports. As recently as three years ago, houses sold here for less than half of what they could command in the Vancouver area.

First removing the cap of one bottle of beer, Mr. Baker reviews his career, jovially, as is his style.

It began at age twelve, working on prairie harvest gangs near his home town of Regina for a dollar an hour. "Twelve years old and with a homemade wine hangover, sitting on an old Case tractor and making music in my head from the engine noise."

He worked on a Buffalo-Detroit railway, went into the army and made an unspecified contribution to Allied victory in the Second World War, and in 1945 was painting hydro poles in southwestern Ontario for 35 cents an hour.

He came to B.C. in 1946, driving a 1930 Essex which had only one gear left after crossing the Rockies. "She was straightaway and no other way after that."

He remained in the wage economy for a time. His departure from pay cheques came here in Lillooet. The date is uncertain. It was '50 or '51. He is not good at some figures, and now lists his age at 49.95.

At that time, whenever it was, Mr. Baker volunteered to rig a fir spar in the Texas Creek area, the prize being steady work at $1.75 an hour as a whistle punk. Then the mill stopped issuing cheques. He spent two days on a rock crusher of the highways department, picking out big rocks from little ones.

"I never did like that, and I never saw why they wanted to crush rock anyway. There was plenty of gravel around for picking up."

Thereafter he became first a contractor and then a business-man. Contracting was falling timber.

It took him only a little time to drop a tree on his only chain-saw. He and his partner, Don Fraser, were carrying the chain-saw down the sidehill in two buckets when the thought of junk came to his mind.

"I asked Don how much money he had available for investment. He thought a long time, adding up assets, subtracting current accounts and so forth, and he came up with a liquid capital figure of fourteen dollars. Well, with my twenty-two, that was enough. We rented a store on Main Street for fifteen dollars a month and went into the second-hand business. Real fun days."

There have been many fun days in the twenty-eight or twenty-nine years since. Sometimes Noel is leasing buildings to such reliable tenants as the B.C. Liquor Commission, sometimes selling off in a hurry to buy something else.

He is just about as amused about losses as he is about gains, which helps if you're wheeling and dealing.

In Hawaii, from which he is freshly home, he let slip options on two apartments that doubled in price when he wasn't looking, but he kept two other options, so it all balances out.

The tale of his involvement with a mining stock promoter is more complex, but his philosophic understanding of mining promoters is not hard to grasp. "The promoter screws the public, of course—that goes without saying—but what he really enjoys, what makes his heart glow and his eyes light up, is screwing a buddy. They take special courses in that."

And his Uncle Joe was not all wrong about the oil well. He is a board member of a company that has just hit one in Texas. "Only a little bitty well, fifty/sixty barrels a day. But remember, that fifty/sixty barrels comes every day, Sundays and hangover days included."

Soon he will go to Texas and see the well, as befits his position as a board member.

"I will kick a tire and say, 'Yes sir, that is an oil rig, all right.' "

When it is suggested to Mr. Baker that any machine with rubber tires will not be an oil rig, he says, all right, then he will kick the tires of somebody's Cadillac.

None of this explains how you do so well in a town which prosperity largely overlooked for a century or so.

"My advice to others is, the selling price doesn't matter. You can always sell something. It's the buying price that is important."

The Man Who Built the Sky Ranch

BIG CREEK—There are three monuments to Gus Piltz in this country—the Sky Ranch, Piltz's Peak, and the Piltz Foundation. To those who met the man only occasionally and casually, finding him just another dour old rancher, they may each seem oversize. Yet there they stand, monuments.

Of them, the greatest creation is Sky Ranch. It is a carpet of grass laid in a shallow pass between the Gaspard Creek ranges of the mighty Gang Ranch and the scattered wild hay meadows of the Big Creek country. It is a mile high, higher than any ranch has a right to be at this latitude.

People used to say it was the highest ranch in the world. You may be sure this is untrue. So are almost all other claims about ranches which are the biggest, the wettest, the farthest north or south, or the richest. People just like to say such things about ranches.

What is true is that Sky Ranch consistently produced prize-winning lots of cattle at Williams Lake and that at one time it ran 550 head of stock, a very large herd in a country designed for grizzly bears and swamp moose.

Sky Ranch was built by the tenacity, the drive, the determination, perhaps the genius of one man, who devoted one lifetime to it.

August Martin Piltz came to Canada from a German colony in Czarist Russia. His own family couldn't get out of the Ukraine until later and Gus was smuggled in on the passport of a family named Wersh. He had to teach himself to read and write English, and in the great new land we were then he was apparently fitted for nothing more than labour. He began cowboying here in 1912 for Joe Tretheway of Chilco Ranch.

In 1917 he settled on the piece of ground which was to become the Sky Ranch. At that time it was called Big Swamp.

He trapped, bought a few heifers on credit and, in 1918, began forty years of ceaseless work. He drained that swamp.

First he channelled it, hoping the water would run away down Coopering Creek. It didn't. If Gus was dismayed, he was also undaunted. He cut a ditch around the entire perimeter of the swamp, carrying away the mountains' runoff before it could reach the flat land. That worked, but it took more than most men have the muscle or the mind for.

The toughness of Gus Piltz has nourished more yarns in these parts than the man would have had time to live. One will do for an example.

Riding back to his little cabin one night on a half-wild cayuse (all the Piltz horses were half wild) he galloped into a wire clothes line, took out all his teeth, and rearranged half the bones of his face.

He was unconscious for some time. When he got off the ground he went to the cabin, examined his wrecked face, and tucked together the broken bones by hand as well as he could. Then he fainted again.

He revived, caught another horse and rode, all that night and much of the next day, almost 50 miles to the first aid post at Alexis Creek. Being Gus Piltz, he left a note on the Church Ranch gate, 18 miles from Sky Ranch. He had been feeding cattle for Church that winter. He wanted them to know that the cows would be untended for a day or two.

Later he hired help. They seldom stayed long. He was demanding, irascible, sometimes plain mean.

To have lived on moosemeat and huckleberries through the Hungry Thirties was one thing. To hired help of the 1950s it was less understandable that the man who raised prize beef felt he couldn't afford to have both butter and jam on the table at the same time.

When I first visited him in the fifties he served a hot rum. I should have been satisfied that it was not his other favourite drink which was whisky and Cherry Heering mixed in equal parts. I asked if he had any sugar for the rum. "You'll drink it that way," said Gus.

A nephew, Leonard Gildner of Portland, worked for him in

1945. "I got away from there as soon as I had a stake enough to get. He was a hard man to work for. But, then, he is my uncle, my own flesh and blood. He is me and I am him."

Gus never married. He courted the beautiful Hattie Hance, but she chose Frank Witte. For the rest of his life Gus had a particular love for Hattie's children and he was a regular Sunday visitor at the Witte's Circle A ranch on the creek.

That was another Piltz characteristic. He never worked on Sundays. Neither did any man or woman in his employment. It wasn't for religious reasons because he had little if any religious faith. It was the Piltz way.

The nephew, Leonard Gilder, bears testimony to those Sunday excursions to the Circle A.

"As we rode downhill, Gus got gentler and friendlier. By the time we arrived at Circle A, he was a real human being. When we rode back up the mountain at night, he got meaner and meaner and by the time we were at the Sky Ranch he was the same old sonofabitch."

He read avidly and liked discussing politics and all the other ideas of educated men. But he never undertook guiding, packing or other sidelines by which the district ranchers padded their thin incomes. He was a rancher only.

Oddly enough, although acclaimed a good rancher, he was never considered a good cowboy. He rode recklessly, but without grace or style, and he broke many bones.

The last bunch were broken by a horse in 1957. He sold the ranch and moved into Williams Lake.

Suddenly, Gus Piltz found himself with what was, for the 1950s, a modest fortune.

Singlemindedly, he set out to give it away. He provided a few bequests for relatives and friends and had almost $100,000 left. With this he created the Piltz Foundation which gives annual grants to children seeking the education that Gus never got.

With alarming speed he lapsed into senility. Some said it was because the new owners had run an air strip across one of the best hay meadows on Sky Ranch.

He lived on for dim years in a private hospital and finally died January 23, 1967.

The Piltz Foundation money still goes out, year after year. This fall there were fifty-three applicants. The income from the $100,000 fund provided grants for twenty-two.

Gus is buried at the Lake.

He had told his nephew that he was to be buried on the mountain behind the ranch. It was all written down, he said. But when he died there was nothing written down that could be found.

That mountain is Piltz's Peak on our maps. It rises, green-timbered at the base, bare grey rock at the top, above what used to be called Big Swamp. It is not particularly high or graceful, but it is solid, unchanging, enduring.

A Non-Romance
in the Moose Country

ANAHIM LAKE—This is the story of the big-game guide and the
lawyer's wife. They did not marry. It is not a romance. Rather, it
is a highly moral tale—one which will, I am sure, make better
husbands and fathers of us all—females excepted, of course.
The guide now speaks:

She was a customer that I will always remember. Always. She
was a woman who made a very deep impression on me.

Her husband was a lawyer in the United States. She had left
him down there and come up to hunt moose on her own. He
was not with her. As I say, she left him down in the States. I
guess that country could scarcely have operated with both of
them away at the same time.

She talked lots about him, though. I felt just as if I knew him.
His character was made very clear to me. Extremely clear. Absolutely clear. He knew all about how the United States ought to
be run and she knew all about how my guiding business ought
to be run. They must have made quite a pair.

We set out into the mountains with four pack horses. I was
glad to have those pack horses along, quite apart from the way
they so kindly helped us pack our gear into the hills. They were
listeners, those pack horses, and she was a woman who needed a
good listener at all times.

In the morning, she would start talking, a steady regular flow
of words that never dried up until sundown. When she got out
of her sleeping bag, it was just as if you had set the arm of a
gramophone that never ran down. I felt that there was five of us
to listen, myself and the four horses.

And I am proud to say that those horses all took up their
share. There was not a slacker among them. For a fifth of the
time I listened to her. Then I would look one of the pack horses

in the eye. I would not say anything to that horse, I would just look at him. And he would know that it was his turn to listen. After a little time, he would kick the horse behind, or pass the message along in some other way, and that horse would take over the chore of listening to her explain how her husband the lawyer felt about the Supreme Court.

On the first day out, we did not have too much time to hunt moose or even to look at the scenery. From time to time I would point out to her the pretty colours on the poplars or the nice, clear, quiet looks of the mountains. But she would usually just say, "Yes, yes," and then continue to talk about whatever it was that I didn't want to understand. The second day, she developed a thirst about midday. I was not surprised.

"I must have some fresh water to drink," she said.

"There is some water there."

"No," she said, "that water is stagnant."

A mile or two later I found her some more water. No, she said, that water was not fit for human consumption. Every time I found water for her, it was unsatisfactory water. I never realized before that I had been poisoning myself in this country for forty-seven years. Finally, we came to a little creek.

"There is running water," she said. "That is the kind of water to drink." Personally, I had never drunk from that creek, because if flows out of an alkali flat. I started to explain this to her, but she got off her saddle horse, saying that this was good clear water and what a pity it was that I had been so long in finding it.

She remained very active all that night, stumbling over me in my bed roll as she wandered around the camp, talking about her indigestion. Next morning she said she had decided that it was the bacon that did it. I said yes, I figured it was the bacon.

We saw a number of cow moose, but cows were out of season then. She did not approve of that. She explained to me why a bull moose season was very bad game management. She went into a lot of detail on that subject. I have not retained all of what she told me. All I remember is the basic principle that you gun down every cow and calf you can find in order to build up a herd.

Anyway, to everything she said, I would always say, "You may well be right." Then if she pushed me, I would say, "Yes, indeed, you may well be right." This was usually all she required.

I think maybe that was the way her husband the lawyer talked to her also. He had neglected to enclose written instructions when he sent his woman to me, but that was all right. I hit on the formula independently. We had both struck it on our own, so to speak. Anything she said, I said, "You may well be right."

On the way out, we spotted a young bull moose. "I think that is a bull," I said.

But she knew all about moose. "That is a cow," she said. "It has no horns."

"You may well be right," I said, and we rode on. When we got back to camp she said that it had been a very unsatisfactory hunt. I agreed with her on that, too.

Looking for Horses

Because so much of my travel was in the ranch country, horses were a subject that constantly recurred. Some readers even got the impression that I liked horses. Personally, I can conceive of a life which is full, rich, and rewarding and which has nothing to do with horses. On the occasions when I have been obliged to use them, it was in the spirit that second-class riding is better than first-class walking.

But generations of cattlemen seem to feel otherwise about these animals, and although the economic theory is that ranchers keep horses only because they need them to handle cattle, I have met a few whom I suspect keep cattle only as an excuse for running horses.

In any event, throughout much of the Chilcotin, horses replace weather as a means of opening conversation.

BIG CREEK—A few days ago, when it was twelve below up at the Teepee Heart Ranch, Duane Witte suggested that we go looking for horses. Well, I was delighted, of course. As a matter of fact, I didn't really mind very much. Here was a chance to take part in one of the esoteric rites of the Cariboo: looking for horses.

In the Cariboo, it does not matter where a stranger comes to rest, or why. He may be in a moose camp or a duck blind. He may be prospecting or taking pictures of kigli holes. If he but wait a little while, a rider will come by and this rider will say that he is looking for horses.

Sometimes I have told these riders that yes, I did see some horses that day, and have described the horses. Sometimes I have been able to describe the brand. Sometimes I have not seen any horses. One answer appears to please a rider as much as another. He is very grateful for the information, and says, "Thank you," and then says that he must be off again looking for horses, and he leaves.

So last Thursday, for the first time, I was introduced to this mystery as a rider, one of the people who asks the questions.

Shortly after noon, when it was warm, we left the ranch. Duane and his wife Marian rode young paints and I was on an elderly bay, sometimes used to pack moose. The snow lay deep and crusted, and the moose, who were rustling for food in the horse pasture, paused in brushing the snow away with their long forelegs and watched us go by. They appeared to wonder what we were doing. But moose have a naturally puzzled expression, anyway, and possibly they were not really interested at all.

By 1:30 P.M. we had seen two Stellar's jays, three chickadees, one whisky jack, and a Franklin's grouse cock, who came out from beneath the horse's feet with a blast of powdered snow, more like a cannon than a rocket. At 2:00 P.M. we sighted half a dozen horses on one of the long buckbrush meadows of Duane's ranch. They were pawing in the snow for feed, as the moose had been doing—and, like the moose, they paused to look at us as we went past. They were Duane's horses. Unfortunately, they were not the ones he was looking for.

We saw coyote track, lynx track, rabbit track, moose track, and squirrel track. Even our stirrups left tracks as our horses walked through the deeper snows.

There were some of Duane's horses on the meadow that we reached at 3:00 P.M. But these also were not the ones that he was looking for.

Duane rode right to look over a spruce swamp, and Marian and I went to the Big Meadow. We found horses in both places. But these too were not the right ones.

We rode by an old corral built by wild-horse hunters. (Hunting horses is much different from looking for horses. But that is another story.) We rode through the little grove of trees where the rustlers had camped a few years ago. They stole thirty horses from Duane and are believed to have driven them north to the roadless ranges above his ranch.

When it was late in the afternoon, an east wind began to cut at our cheekbones with little pieces of broken razor blade, and we came home to the ranchhouse. We had seen, oh, quite a lot of horses, I would say, although not one of those that we had set out to look for. And that is what it is all about.

The only thing I forgot to find out was why we were looking for them. The thought did not occur to me until a day later, when I was hours away on the road out to Hanceville.

Come to think of it, in all the years of meeting riders in the Cariboo, I have never met one who found his horses, nor one who said why he wanted to find them. What an opportunity was mine! I could have penetrated to the very heart of the mystery! There I was, riding with the man. He was there. An expert. All I had to do was ask the question. But I never asked him.

That is the way a man fritters away the great opportunities of life.

Looking for Horses Again

BIG CREEK—The last couple of days have been spent at Duane Witte's Teepee Heart Ranch in the Cariboo. We were looking for horses. I don't know why. But there is, no doubt, some reason.

Duane's place is at the Eight Mile Meadow. It is eight miles beyond what was traditionally considered the end of the road. However, it is now possible to drive a car to Duane's except for some periods of spring, winter, summer, and fall. A couple of days ago, it was possible—and there, in the yard of his ranch, was Duane. He was fixing the tractor and thinking about horses.

"I am pretty sure," he said, "that my good team is up at the Long Jim Meadow."

The Long Jim being only twenty miles distant, we decided to ride over there to look for the team. What we would do if we found them he did not say. Drive them down to the corral where we could have a good look at them before turning them loose again, perhaps. Something of that sort.

First, however, to save a day's ride, we made a trip down the trail to the Bell Ranch. Sherwood Henry is on the Bell Ranch. Sherwood probably had been in touch with Lynn Bonner of the Deer Creek Ranch. Lynn has a plane. Possibly he had been flying over the range. Possibly he had seen Duane's horses. Possibly he had told Sherwood about it. Think of the time we'd save.

So we drove out of Eight Mile and went down the road and didn't get stuck until we hit the hill on Jack's Mountain. We had to put chains on, and this took two hours because the chains didn't fit. Putting small chains on large wheels requires a great deal of perseverance, deep in the night with no flashlight, and we were very late waking up Sherwood at the Bell Ranch. It didn't matter, however, because although Lynn had been flying, he hadn't flown over the Long Jim Meadow so there wasn't a thing that Sherwood could tell us about Duane's horses.

This ended the first day of the horse hunt.

On the second day, many people had collected at the Teepee Heart Ranch. Harold Nickson of the Old Hutch Place had come to fix Duane's tractor. Lonnie Russel of the Anvil Mountain Ranch, another neighbour, had come to help. Thus, there were plenty of riders—ample to hunt for horses on the Long Jim. However, there weren't enough saddle horses in the corral for all of us. So before riding up to Long Jim to hunt horses, we had first to hunt Duane's saddle horses. They were feeding nearby on Wild Horse Range and Big Opening.

I declined this exercise. Harold, Lonnie, Duane, and his wife Marian went out for the saddle horses shortly after noon. Harold, Lonnie, and Marian were home by dark. They hadn't found the saddle horses. The horses had moved for some reason. Why, nobody knew.

Duane got home at nine. His spurs jingled like Santa Claus' bells when he stepped on the porch, but he wasn't noticeably cheerful. His face had been cut by brush. It is hard to chase horses through jack pine in the dark of a moonless winter night. He had cut track. His saddle horses were moving west for some reason. They were probably heading for Bald Mountain. He didn't know why.

Duane was riding Colonel Ambleman, his Tennessee-walking-horse stud. The stud could detect the stepping holes of the other horses in the snow long after Duane had lost sight of them. But eventually even Colonel Ambleman couldn't follow the trail any longer, so they had come home.

On the third day of the horse hunt, Duane, Harold, and Lonnie set out to find the saddle horses with which we were to look for the other horses which were possibly up at Long Jim Meadow. The saddle horses are probably on Bald Hill Mountain. Either that or they have gone over the watershed to Paxton Valley. If they are in Paxton Valley, it will take—oh, a long time—to get them back.

Unfortunately, I can't wait. I must pull out tonight. However, I am in the third day of hunting horses and I have not yet had to climb aboard a single knot-headed cayuse. It is one of the best horse hunts I have ever attended. And just as productive as any other.

Mustangs and Other Horses

ALEXIS CREEK—The fickle eye of public interest has, in recent years, focussed briefly on the Cariboo wild horses. Wild horses have attracted the attention of ranchers for generations, but the interest of the general public in such matters is always briefer—although it may be, for a short time, far more intense.

The majority view of the ranchers seems clear. They want wild horses tamed, trapped, and sold, or shot, according to merit. They do not want them on their ranges. They say that they are runts which kidnap mares from domestic herds and take them away into the mountains. They say that wild horses breed down the domestic stock. They say that the life of a wild horse is nasty, brutish, and short—and the shorter the better.

Those who love the wild horse bands say there is something splendid about anything wild and free. Should we wipe out the last of the wild horse bands, they say, we will regret it, even as we would regret the extinction of moose, deer, or any other wild creature.

Having had the good fortune to watch a wild band stampeding across a lonely mountain meadow with their broomtails streaming in the wind of their passage, I have been able to develop a sympathy for both points of view. Hence the following observations, which prove nothing.

Much of the argument as to what constitutes a wild horse is spurious. Those who like them maintain that they are the original mustangs which flooded the western plains of North America after the Spaniards introduced the horse to this continent in the seventeenth century. Those who dislike them say that the Cariboo herds are simply domestic stock, run wild. It may be argued that both are correct.

The word mustang is from the old Spanish word *mestana*, which means a domestic animal that has escaped the control of its original owner. In Mexico, the words *mestano* and *mestana* were applied to the stallions and mares that went wild. In later years, Mexican ranchers substituted the name *marron* for wild stock, but in the United States the name mustang clung. The modern domestic horse that runs wild is repeating the pattern of the Mexican ranch stock. Whether the name mustang applies is an academic argument.

As to type, most western ranch horses are descended from the Spanish-Barb stocks. Many types developed. Some, such as the Appaloosa and the Paint, have been standardized for registration during this century, after having long been lumped together under general names such as Indian pony or cayuse.

In the Cariboo, the name wild horse may occasionally be applied to domestic stock that has been left on the range after the closure date in late fall or winter. Usually it is applied to bands of horses that have run uncontrolled for years and have bred generations of unbranded animals. They are of all colours and shapes, but successive generations become smaller and may tend to become dark of colour with the so-called wild stripe on the backbone. The rule of thumb in distinguishing wild horses is their immense growth of mane and tail, the hair of the latter sweeping the grass as they walk. Hence the name broomtail.

Only in the narrowing area of the West that is given over to open-range ranching does the question of wild horse control exist, with the exception of a few isolated groups such as the wild ponies of Sable Island. However, in the Cariboo, the division between wild and tame horses becomes almost indistinguishable. On most ranges, the grazing division of the Forestry Department insists that domestic stock be brought off the open range in winter. Those remaining on the range may be killed (in some areas) despite the fact that they are branded animals.

Wild horse herds develop during cycles of moderate weather. In the late 1940s, ranchers say that a band of at least five hundred roamed the region of Sugar Loaf Mountain near Anahim Lake. The desperate winters of 1949 and 1950 are believed to have eliminated them all. Those who are opposed to the protecting of wild horses say that it is an exercise in cruelty, that in the B.C. mountains all such bands face a cruelly slow death by starvation when one of our severe winters locks up their feed areas in the remote mountain valleys.

Over the years, the wild-horse herds have been thinned by men as well as by winters. Hunting is always done in winter. Some herds are driven into crudely built corrals with long wings. Once trapped there, animals of good conformation may be chosen for domestication. Others may be sold into the United States to be butchered for fox feed.

In other circumstances, cowboys are sent out to shoot wild horses. Bounties are sometimes paid for wild horses, the hunters bringing a set of ears for a mare's bounty or ears and testicles to claim stallion's bounty. It is said that in years past, some hunters found the game department willing to accept moose testicles with mares' ears and that the kill of wild horse stallions reached astounding proportions. This might be true.

No matter what the activity of the hunters or protectionist societies, it seems safe to predict that wild horse bands will exist for many years in B.C. They are continually being reconstituted from domestic stock.

However, as the fences advance and our wilderness shrinks, we may encounter a day when they will no longer exist. Whether this will be a better and kinder thing is still open to debate.

On Old Horses, Winter, and Death

ALEXIS CREEK—Some of us were sitting around talking the other night when the subject of horses arose.

This is winter, when the old gentleman with the scythe passes among the horse herds, making his selections. These selections are usually made among the young and the old horses, for slightly different reasons.

Colts and yearlings do not endure winter as well as mature horses. Some ranchers estimate that only fifty per cent of young horses survive to the age of five. They are inexperienced, more prone to falling into spring holes and to other hazards. Also, their inability to endure severe cold has a simple arithmetical explanation. Young animals have a larger ratio of skin area to bulk. Thus, their body heat dissipates quicker. Sometimes they cannot eat enough to fuel their little bodies against the steady drain of cold.

At about twenty-five another process operates, one less easily explained, except in the two simple words—old age. These old horses may have done their accustomed work in summer and may have fattened satisfactorily in the golden days of autumn. But they will fade during the long winter.

Even if fed grain, these old pensioners who once rustled for themselves will become gaunt as the winter progresses. The snow will lie on their backs. Some will be cast in the snow—unable to rise from a fold of the ground where they have carelessly lain to sleep—and if they do struggle to their feet again they may rise with one side frozen. Ranchers can usually apprehend, before autumn ends, when a horse is facing his last winter. They then sell the old animal to be slaughtered for fox feed, or they shoot him.

We were talking of such gloomy matters here last night with Lester Dorsey of Anahim Lake. He was passing through town with more than his usual speed, the back of his pickup laden

with sacks of grain. On Lester's range there has been heavy
snow, then rain, and then a freeze. These are the classic conditions of a mass starve-out and he was in great haste to take feed
into those icebound meadows.

Last fall, he had forty pack horses and saddle horses in his
hunting territory behind the Rainbow Mountains. When the last
of his hunters left, Lester looked over the herd and selected
those whose work had ended. With one of his guides, he led
them one by one down the meadow and shot them. They were
Red, Brownie, Little Joe, Dago Pete, Old Alec, and Shanaham.

"I would never sell an old horse for fox feed," he said. "I saw
some of those old horses in the yards at Kamloops one time.
They were being shipped down to the States to be butchered. I
decided right then that it didn't matter how hard things ever got
for me, I would never need twenty bucks enough to sell an old
horse for fox feed.

"Shooting them used to bother me. Years ago, I used to hire
fellows to shoot them for me. But I went out in the meadow one
night and found an old horse that had been shot in the afternoon and he was still alive. So that ended that. I always shot my
own after that.

"Still, it used to bother me a lot, up until just a few years ago.
Then I began to feel differently about it. You just take the
heaviest gun in camp—my Ought-Six is pretty good—bring it
up fast, just between the eyes, and pull. Usually, there's only one
kick when they go down.

"I don't believe they ever know what's happening. They're old
anyhow, and it all happens too fast for them to know what is
coming. Just *Bang* and they're down, and there are no more
hard winters."

So we agreed that we all have to go some time, which is probably the tritest statement of the human condition that can be
made.

"In our case," said Lester, "when we die, somebody who never
knew us will make a nice speech about us. You may be the lowest
type man the country has ever produced, but somebody will say
something nice about you. And they'll give you a bunch of
flowers that you can't smell. Quite a thing to look forward to,
ain't it?"

Horse Doctoring

BIG CREEK—A few of us were sitting around in a ranch-house kitchen the other night, just talking, when for some reason the conversation turned to the subject of horses. Horses have almost as many diseases as people. But when a horse is ailing, it may not be easy to tell which of the creature's ailments is temporarily in the ascendancy.

Many arguments arise from this situation. So in a very short time, our host went to his desk, which stands against the wall through which the moose has poked his head, and there found his good old reliable horse-doctor book. This little volume is five inches thick and weighs about as much as the average stock saddle. Needless to say, it contains the details of every malady known to the horse. Wind colic is there; also bots, contraction of the hoof, the strangles, pink eye, founder, galls, and glanders. There is plenty of material here for a long, long evening of melancholy discussion.

But there is more. The authors of *Vitalogy* (as my friend's horse-doctor book is titled) had a vision of world affairs extending far beyond the subject of horses. In fact, of the book's 1258 closely written pages, only 56 were devoted to horses. One might even suspect that my friend the rancher has misread the whole intent of *Vitalogy*. It is my opinion that the authors set out to write a book of comprehensive advice for humans and included 56 pages on horses as an afterthought. For humans, the advice offered is, to say the least, comprehensive.

Here, for instance, beginning at page 1231, is HOW TO SELECT A MATRIMONIAL PARTNER: "Don't marry a girl who hangs around drygoods and millinery stores," the authors say. "To dress extravagantly is a blot on any woman's character."

Now, how many of us had the benefit of advice such as this before our marriage? I ask, how many of us?

The authors of *Vitalogy* leave nothing to chance. They have
included illustrations. There are two photographs showing suitable and unsuitable women. The unsuitable one is splendidly
dressed (by the standards of 1890). She offers the promise, say
the authors, of "a life of sorrow and sadness" for any man so
unfortunate as to marry her. On the opposite page is a photograph of a suitable girl. She has a nose that would split hail-
stones and I personally do not find her attractive, but she is
plainly dressed, which seems to be the important thing.

There is more, much more advice for humans in this old
horse-doctor book. There is a remedy for hanging. The victim
must be cut down, immediately (page 49).

Here is another interesting remedy for another condition:
"Alcohol in any of its forms—brandy, whisky, gin, etc.—should
be drunk largely by the patient. Let him drink freely, a gill or
more at a time, once in fifteen or twenty minutes. Or small
doses, oftener" (page 19). You might think this a cure for sobri-
ety. You would be wrong. It is a specific for snake bites. (Kerosene oil may also be used, but the application is of less interest.)

Baldness? See page 771. The authors of *Vitalogy* have
obtained the secret remedy of the royal house of Germany.
"Burn the soles of cast-off shoes to a crisp, pulverize and mix
with a small quantity of fresh lard, then apply at nights to the
scalp lavishly." After a winter's treatment, you enter spring barefoot—but with any amount of hair on your head.

"I can't say that all the advice is sound," said our host. "There
is one treatment there for a horse sickness which involves pouring one to two quarts of whisky into the horse. I have had some
experience with that sickness and I have found it best to shoot
the horse and drink the whisky for consolation."

With that, the conversation returned to the subject of horses,
and all the other splendid advice available in *Vitalogy* was
ignored. Those interested in other aspects of the book may buy
their own copy. Publishers are Northern Publishing House of
New York and Chicago. Unfortunately, the date of publication
is 1900. It may be out of print by now.

The Wild Horse Hunter

REDSTONE—A conversation with Gay Bayliff of the Chilahnko Ranch turned to the subject of horses. Gay used to shoot them—for pay, as well as for the good of his range.

Gabriel Thomas Bayliff is the second of four generations on this ranch, all of whom have retained some English accent. The first in Chilcotin was Hugh, who swam his first cattle across the Fraser near the Gang in 1887. Gabriel, now the eldest of the B.C. clan, edged into retirement during recent years. He serves as a stipendiary magistrate at nearby Alexis Creek. One son of the third generation, Tony, owns and operates the Newton Ranch, which adjoins Chilahnko Ranch. The other son, Tim, has Chilahnko. Tim lives in the big brown Edwardian mansion that was built by Hugh.

Horses can never be far from their thoughts. Tony is recovering from a severe bruising. A week ago, he was pinned under his horse when it fell on ice. Tim's daughter, Elizabeth, is encased in plaster from head to hips. Her horse ran away during a game of hide-and-seek with some other children and her neck was broken.

Near the original family home, Gabriel and his wife Dorothy have built a small, modern home. It was there that we were talking, over tea and fine biscuits, and Mr. Bayliff recalled his days as a horse hunter. He does not believe that wild western horses preceded the white man in Chilcotin. His father said that the Chilcotin Indians had no horses in the 1880s. Also, notes Mr. Bayliff, an early missionary has recorded that the Indians had no word for horse. They referred to Hudson's Bay men as elkmen, in reference to their use of the horse.

The 1930s was one of several periods in which much domestic stock went wild on these ranges. Mr. Bayliff was one of those hired as government hunters.

"I didn't shoot any extraordinary number. Nothing to compare with Johnnie Henderson, who must have shot well over four hundred during those years. I would say the most I ever shot in one year would be seventy-five."

He was paid seventy-five dollars a month to hunt wild horses and got a bounty for each scalp, the amount of which he cannot recall with certainty. He thinks it was one dollar for each mare's scalp and two dollars for the scalp and testicles of stallions.

"They were always in bands. At first, I was advised to kill the stallion first, but I soon learned that that was wrong. When they were alarmed, the stallion would race around the edges of the band, nipping at his mares and colts to bunch them up. He would round them up and drive them. But it was always an old mare who led them.

"The method was to pick the leader and shoot her. The band would then mill around waiting for a new leader to move out in front and you'd have time for several more shots at them. Then, if you could kill the next leader, they'd stop again."

Hunting in this way, he was able to kill as many as eight horses in a single ambush.

"Your hope in tracking a band through timber was that you would catch them out on an open meadow where you could shoot. The stallion would hang back. He was the lookout. I don't know how many times I've tracked a band through the jack pines and never had any more success than hearing the stallion snort as he detected me and began driving them off."

He recalled a long and lonely hunt on a winter's day when he had outsmarted such a stallion by circling the band's tracks.

"When I got to the meadow, there he was, watching for me on their backtrail. I shot him with the 300 Savage and it was a good shot, a heart shot. I heard the bullet hit. He just kicked up his heels and began to round up his band as usual, racing around the edges, nipping and chivvying them. Then suddenly, he just somersaulted. He was dead before he hit the ground. In a sense, he was dead the moment the bullet hit him."

So we drank tea and looked out across the frozen valley of the Chilcotin and at the black hills of pine beyond where, now as formerly, a few horses returned each year to the wild.

"How he used to hate hunting horses," said Mrs. Bayliff. "How he used to hate it."

Horses, Horses, Horses

WILLIAMS LAKE—*The following notes were taken from old cigarette packages, credit card receipts, corners torn from* Western Horseman, *and similar palimpsests. Some were hard to read, and possibly there is no truth in them. Who can say?*

"He was the best horse I ever owned. The best horse I ever will own. Maybe he was the best horse I ever deserved and maybe he was better than that.

"He was a wild horse. Dad and I trapped him in Dick Meadow when I was a kid. We took him home and broke him. I called him Satan.

"There is any number of things I could say about that horse, but I suppose at least half of them would be lies. It is true that I rode him sixty miles to a dance at the Gang one night, but lately when I have told this story it has stretched out to seventy and even ninety miles, so I suppose I am getting on to that age when the truth is hard to remember.

"One thing I can say in all truth about Satan. He had a tremendous dignity. Even after we had been together for years, I could never afford to ignore him. Why, when Satan was twenty years old and had been my horse all those years, I couldn't walk up behind him without talking to him. If I did, he would still nail me with his heels.

"He could kick a man faster than any horse I have ever known. He could bite too. He was fast in every way.

"The important thing was, he had dignity. You could never take him for granted. You had to speak to him like an equal. Otherwise, he let you know that he was not an individual who could be taken casually.

"He was thirty-two when he died. He was the greatest horse I ever knew. I will never have another like him, but then I probably don't deserve to."

A former game guide speaks:

"We had some hunters back in the mountains and we ran into a wild-horse band. They were in a box canyon, so we spotted the hunters around the side and told them to shoot. Well, there is nothing wrong with that. We wanted to be rid of the wild horses. They shot them all down, the stallion, every mare, every colt. They were all down dead in the meadow.

"There is nothing wrong with shooting horses. I've shot lots of horses. But I was disgusted."

A rancher bringing saddle horses out of the corral for dudes to ride:

"That one? She's fine. She's been rode lots of times. The only trouble is, everybody who ever rides her gets bucked off."

Another rancher:

"He's fine to ride, but peculiar. He never bucks anybody off until he is at least five miles from home."

The greatest horses the Cariboo Country has ever produced are orphan colts. Orphan colts are found abandoned in spring holes and are hauled out with ropes, caked in mud of the consistency and tenacity of glue.

They are found—thin, knobby-kneed, stilt-legged—in empty meadows from which their mothers have been removed by the attention of bears or of a city hunter who cannot distinguish between a moose and his own grandmother.

These orphan colts are brought to the home place. They are fed milk and calf supplement by ranch wives. Ranch men stand at the back porch and expound on the vast potential of these little orphans. They distinguish in them all the best qualities of the quarter horse, Appaloosa, Arab, Barb, and Andalusian stocks from which they have sprung.

Given time, orphan colts grow up. As a rule, they turn out to be just another cayuse. They are turned out on the range and forgotten or, with luck, sold to the American who just bought the ranch next door. But the first year of two of their lives, they

are visions of glory. Every place requires such visions from time
to time. This may explain why the finding of an orphan colt is
such an enjoyable experience.

What can compare with the vision of glory? Everybody needs
one. This year's orphan colt may go, but another will be provided next year from the rich breast of nature and life will
continue, nourished by hope.

Chilcotin's
Last Great Horse

CHEZACUT—One of man's trials in visiting Chilcotin during the winter is that you are expected to admire everybody's damned old stud horse. It is a problem in the three other seasons also.

I have always said, "Yes, that is really a horse." It is a statement that is both honest and sincere and is usually good enough.

This trip, however, it happens that there has always been some neighbouring rancher present while the stud was being shown. What was once merely disinteresting became confusing, and if it weren't for a painter named Charley Russell my understanding of this mystery would be considerably less. I am grateful to the late Mr. Russell.

Over the week's earlier stud horse talk I draw a veil of sorts. I name no names. There is enough strife in this world.

We stopped the car in the Kleena Kleene area and looked into a corral where an Arab stud was reported to live. He was there and he was an Arab.

I never knew there was so much wrong with Arabs. They are dainty. They keep their heads too high and you can't see where you are going. They can't see themselves. They won't do.

At another ranch, we admired another stud. He looked like a dun but the owner said he was a buckskin.

It was a horse all right, but when the owner was not present a neighbour remarked, "Stud, hell, he wouldn't make a good gelding."

In the Anahim Lake country, the blood of the quarterhorse infuses stocks that would otherwise be known as cayuse. Privily, it was pointed out to me that these are Bulldog Quarterhorse, all right for cutting contests and other arena games but no good if you've got work to do farther than a quarter of a mile from the bunkhouse.

Once there was even criticism of a stud before the owner's face.

"I had two of these but I didn't need two so I sold one," said the owner. A neighbouring rancher told him, "If I had two studs like that, I would sell two of them."

It wasn't until coming here to Randolph Mulvahill's ranch— the Old Copeland Place, as it's called—that some of the mystery about great studs was blown away.

There are no great studs left in the Chilcotin, said Randolph. They are gone. All of them. All gone. There is none left. Not one. They are finished and done forever.

The great Chilcotin horses, he said, all originated with a Hamiltonian standardbred stud imported by one of the first big ranchers. It cost $6000, at a time when that was a lot of money, and was resold years later to a Redstone Indian at $4500.

Crossed with cayuse and Percheron, this fabulous sire spread strength, stamina, brains, and beauty over all the range west of the Fraser River.

The strain not merely petered out. It disappeared. There was a trace of the blood in his own stud, Randolph said. This might make his stud the best in the country but that wasn't saying much for it because the ancestor is so much greater.

Several of us were so instructed in the Mulvahill living room, which happens to be plastered, wall by wall, with Russell prints.

Russell outlived his rival Remington on Chilcotin ranch-house walls.

Remington's scenes were vibrant with action but Russell's, although often sentimental and sometimes melodramatic, have a detail that earns them undying respect from horsemen.

So it proved among the little band of ranchers gathered there that night.

Somebody's eye was caught by a Russell that depicts a bunch of cowboys riding over sagebrush hills in the American Southwest. One rode a big white horse.

Look at that for a horse, they said. A sliding blind at his eyes—he's so rank you can't get aboard him in the morning if he sees you first. And he's the only horse in the bunch with a hackamore; the others are all spade bitted.

As anybody could see, that horse had piled his rider just a few minutes before Charley painted the picture. There were spur gashes on his withers and there was blood on the rider's face.

There was some disagreement about whether the horse was just about to unwind again or if he had been bucked out into a passable gentleness for the rest of the day. It was all in the set of his legs and the way he held his head, and it was debatable, as you could tell by the way the rider held his lines.

There was no disagreement, none, that here was a truly great stud—mean, rank, treacherous, a horse that would carry a rider through all the fires of Hell and come out in the sunset of Eternity as snorty and as ornery as he was at the dawn.

So there is, you see, one truly great stud left in Chilcotin, but he is hanging on the wall of Randolph Mulvahill's living room.

Conversations at a Stampede

WILLIAMS LAKE—Conversations with a cattleman . . .

Many people go to the Stampede to watch the riding but in the arena very little happens except that some riders win money and some lose.

For some, the focal point of a stampede is the front seat of a pickup truck, somewhere on the grounds, where conversations of high importance are conducted and the refreshments are passed around wrapped in the original brown paper napkin.

Talks at this high level are also held at the hamburger stand, at the horse corral, or in the first aid office—almost anywhere except in the arena where conversation may be hampered by dust, yells, snorting saddle broncs, feedback from the loudspeaker system, and musty jokes told by the bullclown.

The price of beef is a handy subject for conversation. It always has been.

Don Sutherland remembers 1932 when he cowboyed for Ike Sterling at the Diamond S Ranch at Consul, Saskatchewan.

"Ike was shipping and he said, 'Don you better throw them two steers of yours in with the lot.' So I shipped my steers with his bunch. They would weigh, I suppose, 1500 pounds altogether and be worth about six hundred dollars at today's prices.

"What I got back was a statement of the price they brought, the statement of the railway cost, and when all the dust was cleared away I ended up owing $3.19 to the railway. I never paid it and I've gone through all the rest of my life with my credit ruined."

Bill Pulver, who has a little place called Hidden Springs on the Dog Creek Road, also remembers the Hungry Thirties.

"I was cowboying for the 150 then, it was about thirty-two or thirty-three. Bill Laidlaw and George Davidson were buyers then.

"Somebody brought in a good big cow. Eleven-hundred pounds. The only offer he could get was $4.50. Not $4.50 a pound, $4.50 for the whole cow.

"Well, I had some money at the time and I bought her for $5.

"I took her over the hill about half a mile from the ranch and shot her. In the next while I shot five cayoots over the carcass and got $12.50 bounty money from the government."

This shows that even in bad times there's money to be made in the cattle business.

Slim Doran, a cattle buyer, formerly top cowboy at the Dufferin Lake Ranch, speaks of the founding of the town of Merritt:

"Big, modern town now. Few thousand people I guess. There was three good ranches when they put the town there. There was Charters, an Englishman, Vought, I'm not sure how you spell his name but I think it was Vought, he was a German, and there was Garcia, the Mexican.

"It was wonderful ranch country. They ran a railroad into it and the town grew up and the ranchers are gone. Three perfectly good places ruined, just to make another town."

Asking a rancher how many cows he has is about as polite as asking another man how much money he has in the bank. Not only is it impolite, you wouldn't get the truth anyway because what he tells you might attract the unwelcomed attention of the Grazing Division of the Forestry Department who assesses his range fees.

If the subject is raised the conversation goes like this:

"How many head of breeding stock have you got now?"

"I'm running eighty."

"Well then I'd mark you down for a hundred and sixty."

"How would it be if I would say a hundred and ten?"

John Sulatyski, Manitoban, age 35, single, homesteaded Deception Creek near Boss Mountain in 1966 and is now trying to establish himself as a rancher. He has one of the one-figure brands which are now being issued again after a long period during which only three-figure brands were acceptable. His is the peace symbol.

"Why should people in the town be telling me what I can do? I don't tell them what they can do.

"All I want is to be left alone to develop the country. That's how this country was built—by a few little guys who were producers and went out and did things themselves.

"The newspapers haven't got any time for us. Their big circulations are in the towns. The politicians don't care about us. We haven't got enough votes to count. Everybody listens to the people in the towns, but the people in this town wouldn't be here if we weren't out there. It's damn well not fair."

No Drunks, No Fights, No Policemen

WILLIAMS LAKE—Lawrence Gladue's favourite memory-of-the-moment is when he was bouncer in the Lakeview Hotel beer parlor.

His thirty-four years have been generally interesting. A big, 200-pound man with a heavy face, a blend of Cree, French Canadian, and Sioux, he has been a West Coast fisherman, a civil servant, a politician, and a sawmill boss. He has a commercial pilot's licence and does aerobatics for fun. At present he is vice-president of the Council of Non-Status Indians of Canada and lives in Ottawa.

It being stampede time, the Lakeview beer parlor is a bubbling cauldron, customers lining the sidewalk on Mackenzie Street waiting for a seat. Smoke. Noise. Wet tables. A steady rumbling summer thunder of voices.

"I was a shift boss at the P and T mill, but when I got married I needed more money so I moonlighted here for Randy Bremer. I can say with some pride I was a bouncer for three years and I never ripped my shirt.

"Randy has very simple rules for his bouncers. No fights. No drunks. No policemen. You stop the fights, you get rid of the drunks, you don't call in the police."

This, says Lawrence, was not always possible. Some fights develop that are too large to stop, even with the benefits of karate training.

"I watched a fight developing one day between two sets of truck drivers at two tables. You could see it coming, but what could you do? They weren't drunk. You couldn't tell them they'd had too much.

"All of a sudden the fight was on. Six separate fights, twelve men, all at once. Nobody can step into that. The only thing you can do is look around and see if there's some women or old people nearby and you tell them that if they want to watch the fight it would be better to stand over near the wall.

"After a while the fight just burned itself out. There was some furniture broken, but no hard feelings. They all hauled their tables together and started drinking their beer together."

The art of beer parlor bouncing, says Lawrence, is to avoid being rough and tough. Almost anyone who is drunk or on the fight can be eased out of a beer parlor.

"There's the odd guy who wants to fight you. Then the important psychology is that you never do what he expects.

"Maybe he slaps your face. He expects the normal reaction from you. You'll put up your fists. That's what he's expecting and he has his next move planned, so, whatever you do, you don't put up your fists. You break up his plan and run it your way."

There were some who taxed Lawrence's ingenuity.

"There was a huge fellow one day sleeping at the table. Big. One big mountain of muscle. Randy wanted him out because he made the place look unsightly, sleeping there.

"I went up and just gently suggested it was time to go along. He just waved the back of his hand, pwiisht, he brushed me off like a fly.

"He was big, strong, mean, and sitting down and how I was going to handle him I didn't know.

"What saved me was a tiny little woman. She came in, she grabbed a handful of his shirt and began whacking him on the face, front hand, back hand.

"Apparently he was late for dinner again. He just got up and followed her out.

"I never had my shirt ripped. Nobody waited for me outside to pick a fight with me. Nobody let the air out of my tires. It was a smooth operation. I quit it when I became the provincial Liberal candidate in the 1971 election. It didn't seem too suitable to politics.

"Good pay. A six-hour day. On a stampede weekend, with double pay, I'd be up to fifty bucks.

"Once I got tipped. I was easing somebody out the door and he reached in his pocket and handed me twenty cents. 'Thanks,' he said, 'I've been wanting somebody to do this to me.'

"Fifty dollars a day and, over the course of three years, a twenty-cent tip besides. A job I'll always remember."

Midnapore's Copper Pete

A ghost came up the other night and asked if I remembered him. Remember him? God, I could never forget him. The autumn winds still whistle through the hole in my heart which was left when he died.

His name was Midnapore's Copper Pete and he was a Chesapeake retriever, with all that the name implies. He was big and uncouth, he smelled like a wrestler's socks, and he would never undertake any action or gesture to try to make himself loveable.

In puppyhood almost any dog, any species, is winsome. When Pete was a pup he was aloof, stubborn, and highly resistant to affection. He had already made up his mind about life. It was a serious business.

He entered our family at the age of six weeks, assessed us all, one by one, with eyes the colour of lemons, and came to the conclusion that we were flighty and unlikely to amount to much in this world. At ten weeks he began to accept me as worthy of companionship when I shot a crow and let him carry it. Most dogs don't like to pick up crows but Pete liked to pick up anything.

For the rest of a long life, this was his one joy—to charge out through the brambles, the ice, the cactus, broken glass if it were there, and pick up a bird to carry back in his mouth.

Ducks, geese, and grouse were his favourites but in the off season, when for reasons he could not comprehend I did not shoot them, he would pick up most anything else—a bag of groceries, canvas dummies or sticks. He did not even disdain to carry the occasional frog around.

Frogs have an alkaline poison on their skins which is supposed to discourage other species who may have designs upon their persons. Pete did not like the poison, but at summer camp, there being nothing else around, he would deliver live frogs to our children. Bitter saliva would stream from his chops, but his tail would be wagging and his eyes alight with the pure joy of a happy craftsman.

He had enough strength in the jaws to sever the average crowbar, but in retrieving he was gentle. On one day of note, the frog supply having run low, he delivered to the cabin the nest of a killdeer, complete with small birds. Neither the nest nor the nestlings were harmed. We carried it back to the frantic mother, and as far as we know she raised a clutch of young who doubtless spent the rest of their lives talking about the time they lived in a Chesapeake retriever's mouth.

He would also dive into the lake to retrieve rocks on the bottom and became adept at swimming underwater, nothing showing above the surface but the tip of his big otter-style tail. This may have damaged his hearing in later years, although one could never be sure if Pete had become deaf or had simply ceased listening.

He killed chickens regularly and at first ostentatiously. After I beat him for it, with much pain to my hands and little to him, he agreed to never again kill a chicken while I was looking at him. The chicken mortality rate in our neighbourhood remained high.

He lived outdoors and clearly preferred to. He was impervious to wet, to cold, and to fatigue. He also put up an invisible but impenetrable barrier to any attempt to teach him manners that were not connected with hunting.

He always appeared to ignore the children and if youngsters teased him he would walk away instead of protesting. He was aware of them only in that when a stranger approached, a large portion of Chesapeake would be found standing quietly between that person and our kids. There was never any growling, but the message always got through.

My wife, like many hunters' wives, seemed to fall heir to much of the business of feeding him, giving him water, grooming him, and worrying about his health. He accepted all this as his due, but he could never bring himself to show her anything more than a friendly tolerance, because she did not hunt.

His exploits in retrieving were such that people wouldn't believe it if I told them. I tell them anyway.

He had a great nose, great eyes, and stamina. But above all he had that awesome, singleminded joy in his work.

He would commonly go out into ice so thick that he could only press through it by breaking it with his own weight. If, after crossing the ice to open water, the bird had drifted down the shoreline, he would break new ice to bring it back rather than look for the first channel he made.

He appeared to never tire. He did, however, become bored if there was no shooting. On a bluebird day, a companion and I were hunting on the Mud Bay Flats. There was not a bird in the sky. There was also, half a mile from shore, no standing post against which Pete could relieve his bladder. My partner stood six feet, four inches high . . . the rest is history.

That indomitable personality never altered. It is said that dogs take on the personality of the master. It was said of us that the process had been reversed. Certainly it is true that I came to agree with him about chickens. I hate them to this day. Also, toward the end of our partnership, I found myself coming around to his policy of ignoring people who chatter too much about too little.

At ten Pete went into semiretirement. There was an implicit agreement between us when we hunted—if the water was too cold, the brambles too thick, he might honorably decline to work. He never declined. To the last he charged out like an express train and would offer to fight younger and stronger dogs who tried to beat him to the bird.

At twelve he went into full retirement and spent his days sleeping, nose and feet twitching as he dreamed about what a heller of a retriever he had been.

Finally came the day he gave a deep groan when I helped him into the car to take him down to the beach for a walk. The old body couldn't work any more. It had become a burden to him.

If I ever did anything to repay that magnificent old friend I did it that day. I took him to the veterinary who put a needle into the vein and Pete slipped out of this life without a quiver, without a tremor, without one instant for regretting the things he might have done but didn't.

Five minutes before, when I brought him to the vet's office, he had looked the receptionist over with those old yellow eyes and, coming to the conclusion that she lacked any redeeming quality, he had cranked one stiff old leg into the air and peed on the corner of her desk.

Flower Child

There was nothing in the conversation to conjure up gnomes or flowers; they were discussing cold, hard money in the Amiable Idiot's house. It was the cocktail hour before dinner and everybody was talking about the hell of not being rich.

One member of the company was taking a course in money management and with the aid of the pocket calculator he was able to prove that if you put $1000 out at 10 per cent compound interest the day your child was born and never touched the money again, the child would be a millionaire before his seventy-fifth birthday.

No flowers in that calculation; instead, the fascination of wealth enough to drown greed and bury all avarice, and all of it done without effort or thought.

The calculator was passed around from one eager hand to another.

A woman who had just turned twenty and had $2000 in her bank account estimated she could put $2000 a year, every year, into a 10-per-cent compound interest account and, at age thirty-five, collect $54,300.

The knock on the front door came many times before anybody heard it.

When the Amiable Idiot opened the door he found the smallest boy he had ever seen in jeans.

The child was so tiny that, had he been a salmon, the Amiable Idiot would have felt obliged to throw him back. He didn't recognize him, but then all the children in the neighbourhood looked the same to him anyway. Some were just higher than others.

In one hand, this inconsequential fragment of the human race held a clump of flowers which had seen their best days. The

Amiable Idiot thought he recognized rhododendron blooms and a red azalea blossom from the bushes on his walkway.

"Do you want to buy some flowers?" asked the child.

"Who is this for?" said the Amiable Idiot, who was regularly approached by sellers of cookies and raffle tickets who were supporting worthy, although obscure, causes.

"It's for ME," said the little boy.

"Oh, I see. And how much are they?"

The little boy thought for a long time.

"It's not for money," he said. "I want you to buy them for a present." He thrust his fistful of flowers forward. The tiny hand was clenched hard around the stems. These were not happy flowers.

"Okay," said the Amiable Idiot, "I'll buy them, but for money. How will that be?"

He handed the child a quarter. The boy put it in his pocket. The Amiable Idiot reached out to take the handful of flowers.

"Not ALL of them," said the little boy. He pulled off one azalea bloom and lay it, stemless, in the man's hand.

The Amiable Idiot returned to the company and told about the little elf who wanted to sell presents, but not for money.

"You've spoiled him," said one of the guests whose views were on the left. "You've introduced him to the profit motive. Why didn't you give him a cookie?"

"That would still be profit," said another.

"You could have put the twenty-five cents in a ten-per-cent compounding account," said the man with the calculator. "That way he'd have two hundred and fifty bucks to remember you by on his seventy-fifth birthday."

And another said, "Any child who can sell a man one of his own flowers and take away the rest is never going to need anybody to look after his financial interests. He'll be a millionaire in his teens."

The girl who planned to have $50,000 at age thirty-five disagreed with all of them.

"He proved to us that money is very unimportant," she said. "And also that making money is a dull, dull, dull subject."

She lifted the limp blossom from the Amiable Idiot's hand and took it outside where she dropped it in the goldfish pool. They all had dinner and talked of other things.

Next morning, when it was early, he found the azalea blossom still floating in the pool. The water had revived it and in the morning light it glowed, a small, perfect jewel on the still, clear water.

Hickory Daquiri Doc

CLINTON—On the main street, the office of the town's only doctor is faced in rough log and along the length of the front is a big board in which are carved the words:

HICKORY DAQUIRI DOC

There is another carved wooden sign on the brief lawn:

BONES SET
BLOOD LET
HOLES PATCHED
BABIES HATCHED

The life of a general practitioner in Clinton is, the doctor reports, varied.

"Had a fellow come in with his head almost cut off. The knife had missed the main artery, but it had cut almost completely through the neck on one side. All the muscles severed so his head was flopped over on one shoulder.

"That was at the house. I told Vera, 'Keep him here. Don't let him stir.' I came down to the office for my bag.

"When I got back he was gone. She hadn't been able to keep him. He'd wandered off looking for some friends to have a drink.

"The friends were passed out and didn't have any whisky left, and he had left them when I got there. Fortunately we're a small town, so I found him in a fairly short time. He was in the cafe drinking coke, with his head lying on one shoulder. That sounds hard but the esophagus hadn't been severed either."

The doctor sewed this patient together and tried, unsuccessfully, to persuade him to enter hospital at Ashcroft. The man said no, and he is today, the doctor says, as good as new.

Frank Campbell, 47, prairie-born, son of an itinerant bank manager, was a GP in North Vancouver for several years. Vera was born in Lynn Valley when that was a place rejoicing in some of the character of a village.

Being afflicted with a passion for horses, the Cariboo, and one another, they ran a dude ranch at Beaverdam for a time and learned lots about banks and interest rates. Since 1971 he had been the Clinton doc and she has learned that sometimes you must clear the dishes off the table and tell your dinner guests to stand aside while Frank plugs holes in somebody there.

They open the rustic office for two days a week and much of the other five is spent in answering the phone at their rented house and in making house calls on the halt and the lame in an area of about 1000 square miles.

Clinton has about 700 people. There are about 1300 in the surrounding area—70-Mile House, Loon Lake, Cache Creek, Big Bar, Gang Ranch, Empire Valley, Canoe Creek, and the rest. Everybody knows everybody else for better and for worse.

One of Dr. Campbell's patients was observed in the town's beer parlor with his intestines protruding. The bartender would not serve him and he went to the doctor's office.

"His girl friend had cut him with a knife and he didn't want any trouble made about it. I pushed the intestines back in and did some suturing. He was one I insisted on getting into the hospital."

As for the ordinary aches and ills that afflict us all, the doc says that any small town GP knows that they are directly tied to economic indicators and the weather.

"There have been times when as much as ninety per cent of the town has been out of work. Then we can't keep up with doctoring in a twenty-four-hour day.

"In May, when it's Clinton Ball time, scarcely anybody is ever sick. Even the weather makes a difference." He pointed to the grey cloud that filled the town. "That cloud's been hanging over us for four days and the office has been jammed.

"Most people's troubles are psychosomatic. You do what you can, but a lot of it is listening to them tell you their troubles."

Ranchers, he points out, are a rather different breed.

"If an old-timer walks in and he tells you that he's had a little trouble shaking a cold, he was in town for the afternoon, and he thought he'd just drop in and say hello ... well, you know, before you ever make the examination, you know it's pneumonia. At least pneumonia.

"Bad times hit ranchers too. Look at the beef prices. The difference seems to be that they get discouraged, but they don't get depressed."

There is a peculiar feature of medical practice here, he says. He knows of no explanation. He knows of no study that has been made of the phenomenon, which is the low incidence of infection.

"I think our office is as sterile as we can make it. We follow all the procedures. But it's only a doctor's office and when I've had to patch people on the kitchen table, well a kitchen is a kitchen.

"In the big city hospitals, with all their elaborate precautions, you resign yourself nevertheless to about four-per-cent infection rate. Since 1971 here I've only had one repair job in which there was significant infection afterward. I can't figure it out."

Out of all this he has got, he reports, two Appalooseys, two Morgans, and a grade mare (for which read cayuse). He is looking for land where they may be domiciled. "I earn about two-thirds what I could get as a GP in North Vancouver."

But it's a good life?

Hell, no. It's a hard life, but enjoyable, says Hickory Daquiri Doc.

The Mule Skinner

FERGUSON—To learn how to be a mule-skinner, you must come to Ferguson and ask Seldon Daney, the postmaster. No doubt the information may be picked up elsewhere. But why? Ferguson is such a lovely place to visit—even if, as Mr. Daney said, one arrives forty years late.

Ferguson lies at the northern end of the Lardeau country. The mountains around it form a cupped hand, and Ferguson lies in the palm. A narrow little road pokes between the fingers of the mountains and connects Ferguson to the Galena-Kaslo road. It is the same little road that the mule-skinners used when they freighted in to supply the four hotels, the many stores, and scores of Edwardian and Kootenay Rustic houses which made up Ferguson.

Now Ferguson is a ghost town, known to few except the Columbia Metals promoters, a few old-timers of the Kootenay, and the Canada Post Office. On the day of my visit, the only inhabitants of Ferguson were the postmaster and his wife, Edna. There is but one other resident. The last hotel still on its feet sags beneath its light blanket of snow. All the buildings, except the two occupied, are boarded up. Most of them have long ago been flattened by the snows and their timbers covered over with new forest.

But as to mule-skinning . . . Mr. Daney is by far the best man to ask for information. His father came here as a freighter in 1897 and never left. Seldon Daney was born here, and has left only briefly. He remembers the mule teams slightly, and the six-horse freighters which succeeded them very well. He has freighted himself, first with horses and later with trucks. He still operates a trucking business over these roads.

Whether operating a horse or a mule team, Mr. Daney says, some essential equipment was needed.

A claw hammer is one such article. The claw hammer was used to open Borden's condensed-milk cases.

Years ago, before the trading stamps, before industries began attracting cutomers with lottery tickets, Borden's conceived the idea of placing premiums in each case of condensed milk. These premiums, when accumulated in sufficient number, could be traded in for Ingersoll watches and other valuable and useful articles. It is open to question whether the merchants of Ferguson ever realized this, despite the fact that they sold much milk.

Part of a skinner's salary was obtained by opening each case of Borden's, removing the premiums, and neatly nailing it shut again. The cases were wooden, so it will be seen that a skinner must have some skill as a carpenter as well as an ability to talk to horses in a language that they can understand.

A gimlet was also necessary equipment.

In Ferguson's early days, whisky was imported in big barrels. To remove the whisky preparatory to delivery at the hotel, it was necessary to loosen one of the iron hoops and tap it to one side. In the clean wood left by the shifting of the hoop, a small hole was drilled with the gimlet. From this hole, a clean, well-washed bottle could be filled. Sometimes, more than one bottle was filled.

A plug was whittled to fit this hole (all skinners must carry knives), the plug was tapped down flush with the stave, and the hoop then neatly replaced. The hotelmen of Ferguson did not note the absence of a quart or two of whisky from a sixty-gallon tun. All barrels slosh. It's expected of them.

Then the manufacturers began shipping their whisky in bottles, each bottle in its own compartment in the case. A compartment for every bottle. Each bottle sealed. Such a crisis had never before confronted the freighting trade. For a time, it seemed as though the business might end, its craftsmen turning to stockbrokerage or some such trade. The crisis, however, was met. The Armstrong Method was introduced.

In loading a wagon, one case of whisky was permitted to drop upon British Columbia. The broken case was held above a large funnel. The funnel led to a clean bottle. Out of the tinkling shards of glass, out of the cute little individual compartments, whisky ran through cracks in the case, into the funnel, and thence to a bottle. Often more than one bottle. When all wastage had been averted, the case of shattered bottles was again loaded on the wagon and delivered to the customer, intact, so that the latter would have no cause to feel cheated.

Here ends the lesson on how to be a skinner. The equipment needed: clean bottles, a claw hammer, a gimlet, a knife, and a funnel. Needless to say, Mr. Daney, son of the owner of the freight line, was not guilty of such practices. He may have other, different sins on his record, but we did not discuss them.

The Bull Named Jimmy Hoffa

MERRITT—To get a muley Hereford bull named Jimmy Hoffa home for Christmas at the Guichon Ranch required five men, two horses, two snowmobiles, one truck, one airplane, and twelve days. You and I may be glad that we don't own that bull. If you're not, I am.

The Jimmy Hoffa affair began about Thanksgiving Day. By that time the winter snows were settling on the Guichon summer range and sixty-one of their sixty-two bulls had made their own way out of the high country and down to the home ranch at the upper end of Nicola Lake. There the cattle winter on bales of hay and their private thoughts.

By November 1 the bull Jimmy Hoffa was still absent. Gerard Guichon and his son Lawrie were mildly perturbed. Jimmy Hoffa was bought last year in Lethbridge, Alberta. He was one of the least intellectual sons of Lethbridge and knew nothing about mountains.

Two cowboys, Joe Pete and Jimmy Michel of Quilchena Reserve, spent the first week of November in the hills, tiring their saddle horses in deepening snows. They didn't find him.

On November 11 Lawrie Guichon, who is also a commercial pilot, rented a Cessna 180 from Kamloops. He, his father, Joe Pete, and ranch mechanic Scott MacMillan flew the hills and valleys of the summer range.

Joe Pete spotted Jimmy Hoffa at the shore of Michel Lake, standing disconsolate in the snow. Michel Lake is about fifteen miles from the home ranch on the wrong side of a high ridge.

On November 12, Lawrie, Joe, and Scott left the ranch at 8:30 A.M. in a truck, packing two Skidoo Alpine Double Track snowmobiles. When the snow became too deep for the truck they unloaded the snowmobiles and set off for the ridge, carrying sandwiches for themselves and one bale of hay for Jimmy Hoffa.

They found him standing in three feet of snow at the lake-shore about 1:30 P.M.

He had eaten all the swamp grass left uncovered by snow and had turned to chewing willow twigs. He had slimmed down from his normal 2200 pounds to about 1900. He was sulky.

They fed him. Then, one snowmobile behind, one ahead with a man throwing handfuls of hay over his shoulder, they induced Jimmy Hoffa to start down the trail for home.

The bull travelled only about a mile. Shortly before dark the men left him with the rest of the hay and made their own way back to the ranch-house.

November 13 they went back at dawn in the snowmobiles, one of which broke and had to be repaired with haywire and prayer. The bull had returned to Michel Lake. That day they coaxed him as far as Frogmore Lake and again, dark approaching, left him.

November 14 they prodded Jimmy Hoffa 1000 feet up to the Frogmore Ridge, from which he might look down upon the warm valley of the Nicola where the winter feed was stacked waiting for him. A carburetor on one snowmobile had to be repaired that day.

November 15 they returned at dawn to find that Jimmy Hoffa had come down from the ridge, but the wrong way. He had headed back for Frogmore Lake and starvation. They got him up and over the ridge again.

November 16 Pete, on saddle horse, brought him the rest of the way home where he now eats hay instead of snow and treats the sixty-one other bulls with ill-concealed hostility.

Jimmy Hoffa is not the bull's real name. He is a purebred with a long name registered in the Canadian livestock records. The Guichons call him Jimmy Hoffa because he doesn't do much work himself but he prevents others from getting their work done.

The Cariboo Alligator

WILLIAMS LAKE—While scratching an irritating itch of the mind with the thin toothpick of memory, I find I have dislodged a morsel of Cariboo history that is almost forgotten.

Almost forgotten, but not entirely forgotten. Dozens, scores of men attending this year's Williams Lake Stampede will, I am sure, recall these events. They are a portion of history which is not really lost. Rather, they have been mislaid. Men have failed to note their passing, failed to note that they have slipped imperceptibly out of the present and into the forever-frozen area of human affairs which we call the past.

The events I would like to resurrect here—and I trust some eye will distill a tear for their memory during stampede—are the great annual alligator migrations which were so striking a feature of life in the Cariboo country a few years ago.

The alligators were shy creatures—modest, unassuming, and unspectacular except during the fall migrations. Their northerly drift in spring out of the Okanagan was seldom noticed. They had, as a rule, paired up before crossing the Coldstream Ranch at Vernon. They moved furtively and usually by night. Not surprisingly, the pairs were interested only in one another as they made their way north to the nesting grounds.

Their favourite grounds were Miocene, Puntzi, and Anahim Lake. There were also small summer colonies at Nmiah Valley, Spain Lake, and Australian Bar. No doubt there were scores of other regions which they inhabited during the summer season, but no reliable records were kept in those districts. The country was large and the Northwest Alligator (*Alligator caigator impulsivus*) was a small species. The immensity of the land swallowed them up.

Occasionally the roaring of the bulls might be heard on a June night, as they fought for the privilege of associating with their neighbour's wives. But these were the only sounds. The females were silent. An admirable quality, since lost to the country. Females laid, according to status, 29 to 68 soft-shell eggs in mounds of rotting vegetation. The young hatched, usually, just before the Anahim Lake Stampede. They were not trapped. The pelts were poor during breeding season. Occasionally, their omnivorous appetites would lead them to devour a stray dog or an extra child. But they posed no threat to stock, and cattlemen therefore considered them harmless.

Alligator impulsivus was accepted as being just another variety of Cariboo fauna, no more surprising in its presence than the white pelican or the eastern brook trout. They were not popular. But neither were they feared or disliked. In terms of general interest, they ranked ahead of provincial secretaries, but behind university presidents.

Only in autumn, during the great migrations, did they attract any general notice. This migration preceded that of the sandhill cranes, but was usually a week to ten days later than that of the white pelicans. It was led by the bulls, followed by the cows. The young, those which had not already been eaten by their parents (*Alligator impulsivus* was a notoriously sloppy feeder) came last.

The young were, by this time, little more than fourteen to sixteen inches in length. But they were robust, their lavender-tinted bellies swelled with the ripgut hay on which they had been obliged to subsist for the first weeks after hatching.

The movement was generally confined to the creeks. But the general flow of the creeks in Cariboo is westward—an error of Providence which has not yet been rectified. The alligator swarms were bound south to the Columbia River, not west to the Pacific Ocean. As a result, the streams of the migration were obliged to travel overland frequently. Short in the leg but heavy in the claw, these columns of migrating reptiles scoured rocky trails across the grasslands and through the jack pines. These trails were deep, rough, and narrow.

Many of the old alligator tracks can still be found. The Chilcotin Road, for instance, was originally an alligator track. Many sections of it remain unchanged to this day. The Chilcotin strain made its crossing of the Fraser just below Christine's Cabin at the edge of the original Home Valley of the Gang.

At the confluence of the Chilcotin and Fraser rivers, they would meet the contingents out of Australian and Miocene and there would be a brief but colourful frolic.

The migrants then moved overland through the Place Ranch at Dog Creek, travelling, usually, between the hours of 3:00 and 4:00 A.M. The roaring of the bulls, the harsh clatter of curved claws on the gravel, and the thump of heavy tails on the sod—all these sounds made a clamour in the night. But the residents paid little heed. "It is just the alligator migration going through," men would say, any who chanced to be awake in those small hours.

Suddenly the migrations dwindled. A few people began to comment that there weren't as many alligators as in the old days, but such comments drew little attention. By the time it was apparent that the population was facing extinction, the trend had become irreversible.

The provincial game department did everything in its power to preserve the species by opening a hunting season on cows and calves, but they were apparently too late in taking these heroic measures. The race was doomed.

Why, we do not know. Perhaps it was a change of climate or of vegetation, perhaps new diseases and predators. Perhaps it was simply the advance of Hydro, blacktop, loan sharks, and other appurtenances of civilization. Probably it was a combination of all these factors which combined to extinguish the race, thus repeating the tragedy of the dinosaur colony at Miocene.

In 1958, Martin von Riedemann of the Alkali Lake Ranch trapped one of the last alligators seen in the Cariboo country. It was a small, undernourished male (otherwise he would never have roped it).

The country owes an unacknowledged debt to Mr. Riedemann. He worked hard on that alligator's behalf. He nursed the animal back to health. Its colour improved. It developed into a Bay, with three white stockings. The Riedemanns built a pool for it beside the home place and hand-fed it. It liked Wienerschnitzel.

In June, 1961, Mr. Riedemann imported a female Florida alligator (*Alligator missississipiensis*) and put it into the pool with the male.

"We just hoped that when they saw one another, they would think of something to do," said Mr. Riedemann.

But the experiment was unsuccessful. The male, which had always had a sultry temperament, went cultus. In August of that year, he accompanied some of the cowboys on a party in Williams Lake, checked out of the Lakeview Hotel on the second morning and has never been seen since.

The female remained in the creek until November, 1963, when her life was cut short by a Vancouver hunter who shot her, mistaking her for a mule. As far as is known, she was the last alligator in the Cariboo country.

How little trace of the species remains! There is one faded photograph of one of the Mulvahill boys riding one—they had thrown a saddle on it, for a joke. But that is all.

Let us weep for them. We shall not see their like again.

The Amiable Idiot and the Pack Rat

VANCOUVER—There was once an Amiable Idiot who tried to live in a cabin with a bush-tailed rat. The rat had no objections. It was a tolerant creature.

After a few days, however, the Amiable Idiot became nervous and disoriented. He never saw the rat, but he was always conscious of its presence, for the cabin was permeated by a sulphurous odour—much like that which puffs out of the bottle where the kitchen matches are kept. Also, he recalled, the bush-tailed rat is known as the pack rat and is a creature much given to thievery.

Although it was not his practice to leave diamonds or rubies lying loose in the old log cabin, the Amiable Idiot began to fear for his spoons, his pocket knife, his supply of old beer-bottle caps, and other articles prized by men and boys in the privacy of their camps. The world, he decided, was not big enough for both him and the bush-tailed rat.

This is a sad reflection on human nature. Perhaps the rat had an offensive body odour, but was this a true reflection of its personality? We all have some unpleasant personal traits. As for thievery, it was modest thievery. A regiment of such rats could not equal the larceny contained in a single Shaughnessy income tax return.

The Amiable Idiot piled some Warfarin in a saucer and tucked it beneath the cabin. It is an unpleasant poison, inducing a condition similar to leukemia. The victim goes to water after eating it and there brings about its own destruction. (Never drink water.) That night at 4:00 A.M., the bush-tailed rat rattled the lids on the old stove again, as was his wont. Why he liked to fiddle around a cold stove at that hour of the morning is a mystery still unsolved.

"Ah," said the man, hovering in the pleasant area between dream and wakefulness, "it is your last night, rat. Tomorrow you will be dead by the lakeshore."

He checked the poison next morning. None had been eaten, but the rat had gone to a great deal of trouble to cover the bowl with small chips of wood. Being an idiot, the man put out a second bowl of poison, believing that twice as much of nothing would solve twice as many problems. The rat filled that bowl with jack-pine cones.

The Amiable Idiot called loudly upon his Maker and swore that he would, by God, christianize that rat, yea though the mountains be laid flat and the rivers flow no more to the sea.

He drove across the wide ranges of Chilcotin, seeking advice. Finally, he found an old friend standing lonely and under a wide Stetson—Sam Mitchell of the Chimney Lake place. He found Sam where one may expect to find a Cariboo man nowadays—in the coin laundry on Front Street in Williams Lake, doing the wash for Nell. She was no doubt busy with roping or branding or something.

Sam grasped the situation in an instant. Yes, he said, a pack rat could be a very irritating animal. Many a man, said Sam, had been tossed out of the Holy Name Society after dwelling with a pack rat. Having thus grasped the situation by the short hair and twisted, Sam then stared into the Bendix, watching his underwear go round and round and round. The Amiable Idiot feared that Sam had forgotten the whole intent of the dialogue.

Sam had not. After ten minutes or so, he spoke again. "Shoot him," said Sam.

For two nights the amiable idiot slept with his .22 rifle in the sack with him. The rat never rattled a stove lid. His odour, however, had become even more offensive, for he had developed a taste for raw onions. He had consumed four and taken one bite apiece out of the other dozen. The Amiable Idiot lost much sleep, waiting for the rat. His eyes became rimmed with red. He developed a twitch. He lost his appetite, even for onions, which were his favourite fruit.

One night he took an onion and peeled it, so it glistened like a small lantern. He placed it on the stove and surrounded it with tin cans, poised so that they would rattle at the footfall of a rat.

At four in the morning there was a clatter from the stove and he knew the enemy was upon him. Kneeling on the bunk, a flashlight in his left hand, a Winchester Model 41 in his right, the dank humours of the night eddying about his bare shoulders, he shone the light on that rat.

It was a delightful little creature. The body was pale brown, the tail bushed almost like that of a squirrel. The face was neat, pretty almost. The eyes big, brown, lustrous. It would be a poor man that did not admire a creature so beautifully constructed. Thinking these thoughts, the Amiable Idiot put the post of the front sight just on the top of the little black nose and holding his breath, squeezed the trigger gently for a perfect shot.

As it happened, he missed. Missed not only the rat, but the whole damn stove. So this story has no ending, except that the bushy-tailed rat is still living in the cabin and the Amiable Idiot isn't.

A Judicial View
of the Cariboo Alligator

MONTREAL—A couple of months ago, when I was in British Columbia, I wrote a column about the great Cariboo alligator migrations. My mail having finally caught up with me at this drop, I find myself indebted to Chief Justice J.O. Wilson of the B.C. Supreme Court for further information on this now-extinct species. Mr. Justice Wilson's letter is as follows:

I am glad that you have recorded some of the facts about *Alligator caigator impulsivus*. Well do I remember the spring night when a couple of them chewed the tires off my Winton Six in front of the 141 Mile House.

You will recall that Schulmann, in his otherwise impeccable treatise, stated that these saurians were indigenous to the Columbia Basin and indeed presumed to name them *Alligator schulmanni columbiensis*. Some state documents recently found under a bed in the Escorial prove him wrong.

In 1584, Jan Vanderploenck, a Dutch navigator in the service of the Viceroy of Spain, found the mouth of the Columbia and ascended the river as far as the Cascades. When he returned to Acapulco, he gave, in his halting Spanish, a glowing account of the new country, stressing its fruitfulness. The Viceroy said: 'Wonderful, Captain, and since it is a fruitful country, you must, when you return there, stock it with my favourite alligator pears.'

Vanderploenck, whose knowledge of Spanish was rudimentary, made the very natural mistake of thinking that His Excellency wanted the land stocked with pairs of alligators. He shipped a deckload of these at the mouth of the Orinoco and took them to the Cascades, where he turned them loose. They bred, portaged the various falls of the Columbia, and eventually made their way into the Okanagan and the Cariboo. Governor Simpson tried unsuccessfully, in the 1840s, to put them down because of their propensity for kit beavers.

Vanderploenck, ironically, was himself consumed by alligators when he fell off a raft on the Amazon in 1596.

In response to this letter, I can only say that the information it contains surprises me. Because the name of the Asian strain, *caigator,* appears in the Latin name of the Columbia alligator, I had jumped to the conclusion that there had been an infusion of Oriental blood into the West Coast reptiles, possibly as a result of some strays being swept off the China coast by the Japanese Current. (There is no doubt that those which once populated the Cariboo had slanted eyes. Numerous observers have recorded this feature.) But I am not prepared to dispute with a man whose research has carried him to Acapulco and Madrid.

I would like to note, however, that all too few students of West Coast history take the pains to put their findings on paper before the last strands of history's hawser are snapped by the pull of time. There must be many British Columbians who remember the great alligator migrations of the Cariboo. Will they speak now? Or will they take their memories, together with the old-age pension and some Dow Brewery stock, to Cuernevaca or Maui or some other place where the value of their information is not appreciated?

The Conservative Anarchist

Now and then, at home, I thought thoughts of exquisite beauty and clarity. These I put on paper, and then burned. Occasionally some found their way into print.

VANCOUVER—It was a day that opened with aces or better, beginning with a pearly sky over Mount Baker. The birds had a lot to say about this, because, having only rudimentary brains, birds treat every fine morning as a new and unforeseen miracle. Birds have no sense of proportion.

On this morning the Amiable Idiot went out to examine the pyrocantha. He wasn't sure that he could spell it, but he knew it when he saw it. He was weak on names, but had a good memory for faces.

There were better things for him to do—running elections, straightening out Ottawa, dealing with the Kremlin—he could have been far better occupied. Nevertheless, he went out and sat on a stone. It was a first-class stone. You could tell that by looking at it. Even without a sixty-day warranty, it was clear that this was a real stone, built to last.

An extra-large, family-size sun came over the horizon from Moose Jaw. It hurried over the ragged edge of the mountains. When it got half a mile or so above the névé on Baker it paused, as the sun does occasionally, and turned from orange to the colour of dairy butter.

The Amiable Idiot was reminded of the dairy butter he ate as a child. Mrs. Art Mosher used to make it. This butter came in round cakes, shaped like haggis. He had never liked it much. The flavour was too robust to be wasted on children like him. Children prefer foods that are bland and tasteless, pasteurized, emulsified, homogenized, vitaminized, activated and zipped, and, if possible, accompanied by photographs of baseball pitchers.

Nevertheless, although he had never enjoyed Mrs. Mosher's dairy butter during the remote days of his childhood, the Amiable Idiot remembered it now on this morning while he squinted at the yellow sun hanging over the mountain, and he realized that Mrs. Mosher had made good butter.

His wife opened the living room window and said that everybody else was eating breakfast. In fact, this was not true. Half the world's people were asleep and a quarter of the others fighting. What his wife meant was that their particular family was eating breakfast, a rather small sampling of the three billion humans who are around the place now.

However, women commonly look at the microcosm while their husbands are thinking big. So the Amiable Idiot answered kindly. All he said was that he did not care for Wheaties, Germies, Crunchies, Whoopsies, or Cracklies this morning. She closed the window.

She was not surprised, because she knew that he had not eaten anything shot from guns since the Japanese shelled Estevan Point. He was not a pacifist, just a conservative who wouldn't eat even ordinary bacon for breakfast but insisted on slab bacon, preferably back bacon. She opened the window and said, "You are an old conservative."

"I am not an old conservative," he said. "I am a middle-aged anarchist. I stand well to the left of the Peking Communists. I believe that any sort of government is wicked, just because it is a government. Of course, being a reasonable man, I am prepared to compromise. I can accept government of groups of twelve people or less. But anything larger is bad."

"Well," she said, "you can count. There are less than twelve head of stock in this family."

"Why do you always make everything personal? I was attempting to deal with an abstract principle, which is simply that for one human to interfere with another is essentially evil. We only tolerate it because we have to. It doesn't make it any less wicked."

"I hope you know what it is doing for your sciatica, sitting there on that cold stone before the dew is off the grass."

"The effort of people to control one another is the basic evil in man. Nothing is so foul as supergovernment. Look at that poor worker bee."

There was a worker bee, one of the early starters, which had just gone on shift on the pyrocantha bush. "I have been watching that bee for some time. He has no sense of purpose. He is just putting in time. He doesn't take the blossoms in order, as he could do with far less flying time. He hops from one end of the bush to another."

They watched the bee. The bee carefully worked each blossom on a sprig, one at a time, in proper order.

"He's only doing it because you're watching him," said the Amiable Idiot. "Even now, he's only diddling around. I don't think he's collecting any honey at all. He never flies back to the hive. He just pretends to be working on the flowers." At that moment the bee turned away from the bush and flew straight NNE, as though on steel rails.

"I don't see anything wrong with that bee," she said.

The Amiable Idiot went into the house and drank coffee and discussed Gerda Munsinger and other girls whom he had not known.

Koolatilik, ES-542

I met Judge Sissons only once, during a summer visit to the Northwest Territories. Since then I have learned that lawyers and judges find his decisions appalling and that the mandarins of Ottawa found him intolerable. Even without such recommendations, I would have respected the old man.

He is dead now, and it is too late to tell him that. But since he lived by the Presbyterian principle of self-judgement, my approval or disapproval would have meant little in any event.

YELLOWKNIFE, NWT—Judge J.H. Sissons of the Territorial Court keeps in his little office here a collection of soapstone carvings which depict the most notable cases to have come before him. All are the now-familiar Eskimo sculpture, but all have a significantly different aspect from the jolly little carvings that sell in the art shops. Almost all of these roly-poly small figures are tensed in pain or sorrow or anger. Some are rigid in death. They are stabbing one another, shooting one another, or strangling with cords buried deep in their victim's bulging neck. A sad display, but one that is powerfully moving.

The most recent addition to the judge's collection is a large piece. Three Eskimo figures stand in rigid expectancy outside an igloo. A section of the igloo has been cut away by the carver and inside we see a bearded man who is shooting himself.

The man who is shown in the igloo was named Koolatilik ES-542. Those who stand outside are his son, Amah ES-535, and two other members of the Igloolik band, Mangamilik ES-461 and Avinga ES-453. The three men were charged with assisting Koolatilik to commit suicide. The case was tried in the Arctic by Judge Sissons on April 25, 1963, at Igloolik.

In 1962—some time in December, when the sun is never seen in Igloolik—Koolatilik became very sick. He had measles and complications therefrom. He was in severe pain that seemed as endless as the night, and finally became convinced that he was about to become insane.

Koolatilik waited until his oldest son, a man of rather strong mind, had left camp to hunt. Then he called Amah to him and, with him, Avinga and Mangamilik. He explained that it was necessary for him to kill himself. If he lost his mind, he said, he would be a burden and even an actual danger to the little band. They argued with him for a time, but finally agreed to bring him his rifle.

Koolatilik was a pagan, so far as is known, but others of his band had been baptized by the Anglican missionaries. He told the men to go outside the snowhouse and pray while he shot.

He did not make a good shot. As the soapstone carving faithfully records, he held the gun to one side of the back of his chin and only wounded himself very badly.

He called the three Eskimos back into the igloo. This time, Amah ran another shell into the breech of the gun and placed two more within reach of his father's hands. Then the three went outside and prayed again. It was many hours before Koolatilik finally died. He apparently had to fire two more bullets into himself. Amah later told the court that he never heard these shots because he was crying.

They buried Koolatilik—the man named on the white man's records "ES-542"—under a mound of stones. In case the hereafter be not of the shape forecast by the missionaries, they placed his rifle on his grave so that the spirit would be able to hunt. The rifle rested there only a few weeks before the Royal Canadian Mounted Police took it away as an exhibit for the trial.

The judge was flown to Igloolik for the trial. He gets around very well, leaning on his narwhal-tusk cane, despite the fact that he is seventy-three and has been crippled for many years as a result of polio.

"They all wanted to plead guilty, but I wouldn't accept that and entered a plea of not guilty. Of course, as usual, they all took the stand and told exactly what had happened and admitted everything that they were accused of doing."

The verdict was guilty. The three could have been placed in custody of an RCMP detachment to serve their sentences instead of being sent Outside to prison. But this would have deprived their little band of its three best hunters and thus imposed some of the very hardships which Koolatilik had tried to avert by his suicide. So Judge Sissons sentenced them to go back to their band and continue hunting.

He ordered that the rifle be placed again on Koolatilik's grave.

The Man with the Extra Airport

BIG CREEK—Within the tight circle of my friends, the number who have become wealthy remains discouragingly small. For some time, I have thought that none of us will make it.

However, this has now been changed. Bruce Watt has become one of the wealthiest men in B.C. The rest of us may now take heart and try again, casting our thought nobly beyond the meager affairs of grocery bills and payments on the car.

Bruce has, I suppose, been wealthy for some years. But we had not noticed. Perhaps we were misled by the fact that he doesn't have much money.

We did not notice that he was, in fact, rich beyond the dreams of most men. By this I do not mean that he had his health. Health is not wealth, despite what some may claim. Consider how many healthy men are living on welfare cheques.

No, the attainment of opulence is marked sometimes by money, sometimes by an action of some grandeur. A symbol becomes visible, a symbol such as cannot be produced by ordinary men, only by those who are wealthy.

Bruce's abounding wealth became visible in early October this year, at which time it became apparent that somebody had built an airport in his front yard and he hadn't even noticed. I happened to be visiting Breckness Ranch on the day that the news broke. Bruce was not behaving like a wealthy man on that day. He was rummaging his log house for his good pair of pants. He planned to go to Williams Lake, and although he is a man with no more passion for personal daintiness than most of us, he felt that it would be nice to go clad in good pants. And he only owns one pair.

He had learned that day, he said, that somebody had built a damn' airport at his Dry Farm—the summer range he occupies near the junction of the Chilcotin and Fraser rivers. He didn't know who and he didn't know why, but he intended to look into the matter.

That day he went to the Lake wearing his old pants, which are torn in the seat and at the crotch.

A few days later we made our separate ways to the Dry Farm and there found that, sure enough, somebody had built an airfield on Bruce's Crown Grant land. Not on his grazing area, not on some piece of open range where his rights are of a more tenuous sort—but on his own personal property, right in front of the big log house where he and his family live when they are operating this end of his small ranch.

Big equipment had been used. The hollows had been filled and the hills levelled by great earth-movers. The big airstrip ran 2000 feet through his grass—big, raw, bare, and fit to carry anything up to the size of a DC-3. The equipment had departed and so had the crews. But the men who built the field had apparently helped themselves to Bruce's house, and its kitchen was a mess.

Now, how does a wealthy man react when he discovers that somebody has built an airfield in his yard without asking his permission, has messed up his house, destroyed some of his grass, and left without saying thank you. It was plain that these thoughts were going through the man's mind. You could tell, by his serious expression, that he was thinking. After a while he spoke. "By God, Paul, you know, I think maybe I ought to get hostile about this."

That was two months ago. Last week I drove in to Big Creek to discover how hostile Bruce had become. Well, he said, he had been thinking about it. There was something about a man coming on your property without your permission, using your house, breaking your fences, and putting an airport in your front yard that tended to irritate a man. One of these days, he said, he was maybe going to do something about it.

He still owns only one pair of good pants and he still hasn't found them.

After writing this column I became disturbed. Bruce was, after all, an old friend who might be in some legal difficulties. I took the column to his wife, Phyllis. She was then living in Williams Lake, so that the numerous Watt offspring might attend school. Splitting the family is often a routine of ranch life. There may be no other method of combining children with education.

"Bruce may want to sue some mining company on this matter," I said. "Maybe I had better not run it."

"That's the way he is," she said. "It's a good column." I was reassured, but not by that much.

I drove for a few hours to Bruce's home ranch and, after a few more hours of waiting, he came home.

"You had better read this column, Bruce," I said. "If you are going to sue, it might interfere with the court case."

We ate macaroni and cheese, his favourite and almost exclusive dish, and he read the column.

"That's the way it was," he said.

"But will it interfere in a lawsuit?"

"What the hell," he said, "it's the way it was. You ought to print it."

If Bruce has a second pair of pants, I have been kept in ignorance. But he sure in hell has enough airports.

Harry Boyle's Volkswagen

PRINCE GEORGE—Harry Boyle is now the editor of the Prince George *Citizen* and the owner of a beard, a wife, two children, and forty consecutive years of life in this Vale of Tears. A few years ago he also owned the Whitehorse *Star* in the Yukon, an unusual newspaper office in that it was connected to the local poolroom by a covered walkway. Harry considers himself rather adept at pool.

Harry is also the owner of a Volkswagen, sometimes known as the mechanical cockroach or the pregnant roller skate. The events which I am about to set forth involve the collision of Harry Boyle with the massive Volkswagen corporation.

Slightly more than a year ago, while scuttering along the Alaska Highway in his car, Harry became possessed of a strange melancholy, a poignant yearning, a *Weltschmertz*—in short, a thirst. He pulled off the road and grasped a bottle of beer, with which he had thoughtfully provisioned himself before leaving Prince George, and set about opening it.

Harry is an intelligent and cultured man, but his knowledge of simple mechanics is about equal to my understanding of ethnomusicology—which is to say, not very impressive. Noticing that an air vent was located conveniently close to the windshield, Harry levered the bottle cap against the glass. As almost anybody except Harry Boyle might have expected, the windshield broke.

Mr. Boyle took typewriter in hand and wrote to the Volkswagen people. They were, he said, turning out the most expensive and inefficient mobile bottle opener on the market. As a car, he said, his Volkswagen was fine. But as a bottle opener he considered it a dismal failure, badly engineered and full of hazard for a thirsty man. The following letter came back to him from the Toronto plant:

Dear Mr. Boyle:

We have enjoyed your letter which reports your satisfaction
with Volkswagen, but points out the fact that the location of
the factory-installed, no-extra-charge beer-bottle opener has
been kept a secret.

We regret that you succeeded in cracking the windshield, but
assume that you are happy that such an accident did not
occur to a car with a more expensive piece of glass for a
windshield.

In order to best explain the proper beer bottle opening proce-
dure for Volkswagen owners, we prevailed upon our photog-
rapher to record the correct method. You will note that it is
necessary to stop the car and get out, in order to use the VW
bottle opener, but I trust you will appreciate the fact that this
characteristic was designed into the automobile with the safety
of customers in mind.

Two glossy eight-by-ten photos were enclosed with the letter.
They showed the hand of an unidentified Volkswagen customer levering the cap from a Molson's in a crevice which
exists between bumper and bumper-bracket at the front of the
car. In addition to this clear demonstration of Volkswagen's
factory-installed beer-bottle opener in use, the company sent
Harry a multi-coloured marking pen as a sort of bonus.

Harry was now having a splendid time. He sat down and
wrote them again. The pen of many colours was very nice, he
said, but what about the gold watch that Volkswagen owners
were supposed to get with 60,000 or 70,000 miles of trouble-
free driving? He was looking forward to winning that watch and
did not wish to jeopardize his amateur status by accepting the
ballpoint pen.

"I have lost the letter they sent me in return," he says, "but I
can remember the contents. Volkswagen said that with my
approach to mechanical matters, they didn't think I was going to

make it to the gold watch anyway. But they said they admired my spirit and were sending me a Westclox Dax."

Harry still has both the Westclox and the Volks. Both are still working, and so is he.

Harry Boyle has since become a judge, thus remaining devoted to truth, honour, and simple faith.

Dealing with the Likes
of Len Lauk

VANCOUVER—Len Lauk is a television producer, a lad of some forty summers, fair of face and frank of manner, a winsome soul who still continues to search for pearls in his clam chowder. As a television producer, he does very well. All these characteristics are desirable in a television producer. However, they are not in themselves the attributes of a good householder. As a householder he is only moderately successful.

Some years ago Len purchased a house in Kerrisdale. The house had a lawn. He had heard of lawns before, but had never thought deeply about them. He assumed that lawns were—like other features of nature—desirable, different only in that growth was more orderly.

In his first summer of residence in Kerrisdale, the grass on the Lauk lawn grew high. Very high. Very, very high. Len decided that he would have to get one of those grass mowers and cut it. He was pondering this one day while standing on his front stoop, looking out over the hayfield for a few minutes preparatory to his going into the cool lovely shade of his living room where he planned some sack time. A neighbour from down the block came up and engaged Len in conversation. A nice gesture, thought Len, and he responded in a frank and friendly manner.

The grass on the Lauk lawn was certainly high, wasn't it, the neighbour said. Yes, said Len, coming down and wading through it to the gate, he guessed it was the highest grass on this street anywhere. Yes it was, said the neighbour.

They both looked at the hay for a while, and Len pulled a stalk of timothy and began to chew it. That long grass, said the neighbour from down the block, certainly was noticeable, wasn't it. Would it be better if shorter, like the other lawns? Len asked. Yes, said the neighbour.

Len started on a second stalk of timothy before allowing his thoughts expression. The goats, he said, should have that situation taken care of in jig time. What goats? said the neighbour. Why, said Len, had his neighbour not heard of the old people's home being established nearby? The proprietors of the old people's home fancied goat milk for their clients. They were prepared to pay even more for it than for cow's milk. He, Len Lauk, was not one to let opportunity slip by. Soon there would be goats on this lot. He planned to start with two nannies and one billy. Not a big operation, just sort of a cottage industry.

Now that the idea of raising goats had burst upon Len's intellect, he became swept up in a torrent of enthusiasm. He is a man who loves new ideas. Great plans unfolded. The neighbour could not find a chink in Len's flow of conversation in which he could insert a single word.

Income from the goat's milk would more than pay the Lauk family's dairy bill, said Len. It would probably go far toward paying his taxes also. His wife could learn to milk them, a handy skill in any woman. For the Lauk children it would be a splendid experience. He would shift his car out into the alley and use the garage for a breeding pen. There his children could study the marvels of reproduction and observe the sweet affection which nannies show to their kids.

Goats lived for free, so to speak. As they ate the grass, they would deposit manure upon the lawn. From the manure, new grass would be nourished. It was a self-perpetuating cycle, a marvel of nature's handiwork.

After a while, the neighbour left—without saying good-bye. Len picked a dandelion, tested it for smell, discarded it, cast one more loving look at his farm, and went indoors for a nap. He felt that this had been a thoroughly interesting and thought-provoking interlude in what had previously seemed a dull and undistinguished afternoon.

Late one afternoon a week or two later, when Len was resting on the sofa after a hard day of television producing, a gentleman from City Hall came to see him. This visitor was from the Health Department and was interested in goat culture.

By this time, Len had completely forgotten his earlier conversation with the neighbour. He was able to approach the subject as a television producer should, with his mind fresh and free of preconceptions. Viewed in this new way, he didn't like goats.

Who was planning to keep goats? he wanted to know. Wouldn't they smell? Might not the billy goats knock down fences and small children? Wasn't there some kind of a law against this sort of thing in Kerrisdale?

After a while the building inspector went away to call on another resident of the block. Len went back to the sofa and dreamed of walking barefoot through the fragrant pastures of Heaven.

The Prisoner's Return

LILLOOET—The previous time Norman Watson drove into Lillooet he found himself a guest of Her Majesty the Queen in Hotel Crowbar, but time seems to have applied a healing poultice to the wound.

This time, forty years later, he came into town towing a fibreglass trailer behind a Meteor, and dwelt for a spell in the government campsite on the Cayoosh Flats. He lives in Sechelt now and was just poking around.

"Things were different in the late thirties. I just forget the year. Joe Lebeau and I came up here through the Canyon in a 1934 Franklin. We had jobs waiting for us at the Bralorne mine.

"The first night we slept in the graveyard on the other side of the Fraser. The ground, I remember, was lumpy.

"According to the plan—and even in my foolish youth I should have known better than to trust plans—but, I say, according to the plan, we would put the Franklin on the PGE flat car next day and it would take us to Shalalth where we'd take it off and drive it over Mission Mountain to Bralorne where we would make a lot of money.

"Joe spoke a sort of mixture of English and French and our communication had not been as exact as possible. While we were coming up the Fraser Canyon, the Franklin running seven miles to the gallon, Joe had thought I had money for the flatcar and I had thought Joe had the money. In the morning, in the graveyard, we pooled our resources and found we had fifteen cents.

"Well, we phoned the Bralorne boss in Lillooet and he arranged for us to get the Franklin on the flatcar and he gave us a ten-dollar advance on our pay.

"We went down the main street, which was composed entirely of fine dust, and we stopped at a Chinese restaurant which advertised all the turkey you can eat for ninety-eight cents.

"We were just starting to use a couple of the ten dollars when a hand about the size of a single-bitted plow hit my shoulder. It was the local constabulary. Was I the driver of the Franklin? Yes, I was. Could he see my driver's licence. Yes, he could. I was charged with exceeding twenty miles an hour on Lillooet's main street and put under arrest.

"He took us down and locked us up. It's never been clear to me why Joe was locked up. There couldn't have been two of us driving the car.

"We said we wanted to see the magistrate. 'You can't,' he said. 'He's moving today. He's busy.' Anyway, about midafternoon, the magistrate and he came down to hear our case. My case, Joe's case.

"He said it would be twenty-five dollars or five days in jail. I said, 'Thanks, that's great. I'll take the twenty-five dollars.' On reflection I realize that wasn't the best thing to say. Meanwhile Joe was talking in a very impassioned way but, by now, entirely in French, and that didn't add much to the proceedings.

"We discussed an interesting crime called contempt of court.

"They finally came to see that we didn't have twenty-five dollars and that keeping us in jail would cost five days' meals so we hit a compromise. They would keep us in jail until the PGE came in and we could go to Shalalth. We were to remember that we had to come out through Lillooet and that they'd be watching for our Franklin.

"We went back to the jail. We got a cup of coffee, but no food. The train came in at ten to four, ten to five, something like that, and our career as tourists in Lillooet ended. We still hadn't eaten and there was no food on the train.

"Not everything about it was bad.

"I made a five-dollar bet with a man on the train who was going into Bralorne too. He bet that the Franklin couldn't get up Mission Mountain without stopping for water. He didn't know it was an air-cooled engine."

Norman reports that he never did drive the Franklin back through the dusty main street of Lillooet. He sold it to a couple of acquaintances who later used it in an unsuccessful bank holdup. "I had a muscular spasm from laughing when I heard about them trying to outrun the police in the old Franklin."

He quit Bralorne after getting an opportunity to read reports of the silica content in the workings and went on to a few decades of other more profitable activities.

He reports that it's great to be back in the old town, for which he has a sentimental attachment.

Nobody Liked Him
but the People

PRINCE GEORGE—Show me a city mayor who refuses to appoint women to chairmanships on council committees, who says publicly, "We'd all be better off if they stayed home and did the dishes," and I'll show you Harold Moffat who has been chosen mayor of Prince George four times, once by acclamation.

Other notable quotations attach to his name.

Of his city's loyal and faithful public servants he has said, "Fire a few of them—it's a great morale booster."

He opposed giving a grant for a Hallowe'en fireworks display here. "I thought if everybody paid nothing, Hallowe'en might disappear."

While others in central and northern B.C. were gratified that redistribution gave them another seat in the Parliament of Canada, Mayor Moffat, as usual, introduced a fresh thought. "We don't need as many as we've got now," he said. "One or two for the province would be enough."

Most recently he has aroused comment by noting that public libraries burden taxpayers, and he endeared himself to local newspapermen earlier by trying to discourage them from printing city council's agenda in advance. It would be better, he suggested, if the citizens didn't know what council was going to discuss. Then they couldn't pressure the aldermen, whose judgements were better left to rise on the yeast of their own private thoughts.

Now, unless every election in this city of 70,000 has been wildly, grossly corrupt—and nobody has suggested that—Harold Moffat is a very popular mayor. He is popular where it counts—in the ballot box.

Is it all a put on? Does he mean half what he says? All of it?

He is a quiet-spoken hardware merchant. He spends his mornings in Prince's biggest hardware store, only part of the time in a poky office at the back which was painted, long ago, a mournful green. "My father said, 'Don't spend your time in the office. Spend it out with the customers.'" The afternoons he spends at the big new city hall.

He wears a sweater, glasses, and a bland expression. There is nothing notable in his features, except that it is the face of a man who wouldn't scare easily.

Oh yes, he says he stirs people up a bit, keeping women off committee chairmanships and that sort of thing. As for the women issue, he has explained that it doesn't much matter whether it's the mother or the father who stays home, but one parent should always be home when children are small and need them. "That's what I believe, so that's it."

On the same basis of fundamental belief he is taking his city to the Supreme Court of Canada to try to keep the first sex shop from getting a licence "because somebody has to make a stand some time."

We tour his city, of which he is intensely proud, looking at new houses, the new little theatre, the green belts. He is the third generation of the Moffat family in this part of B.C. This year 150 Moffats gathered here to celebrate the one hundredth anniversary of the first Moffat's arrival at Quesnel.

He is spoken of as a right winger, but says he has no party and no object except to co-operate with the present NDP provincial government which is, since the last election, the people's choice.

His city is deep in the business of developing cheap land to sell to home-owners, and prices here are about the lowest in Canada. "Government must be involved in housing. Good housing is a necessity. So are sports and cultural places. They're the heart and life of a city. Until you have them you'll always have a transient population."

He plans to retire at the end of this term in 1976, the year of his sixtieth birthday, and probably won't see one dream come true by that time. He wants to cover the city's main shopping street with a vast glass roof and have a gracious mall for year-round use.

I remind him of one of his memorable statements about Vancouver: "The worst civic government in Canada without a doubt. It's a calamity, the third largest city in Canada governed by that inept bunch." Does he still feel that way?

Harold Moffat considers how he may soften his tongue without abandoning honesty and says, "I'll put it this way. I would never go to Vancouver to look for an idea."

The One-Room School

BIG CREEK—How fares the Big Creek one-room school these thirty-one years after the people here had to borrow two children in order to have enough to open it?

Well, it seems, not badly at all. It has the same teacher as in 1946 and this year, as that year, it has exactly ten students.

Elsie Henderson well remembers the winter of 1943 when she arrived, in January, to be the first teacher in Big Creek's new log school. She was a shy little girl from Saskatchewan who had been hired, she later learned, because the Big Creek school board thought her handwriting was the neatest of any applicant's.

The late Dick Church brought her in from Williams Lake in his truck. He was, as she says, a perfectly splendid man when you got to know him, but he was gruff.

"When I asked him very faintly if we were coming near a rest room while we were crossing the snow on Becher's Prairie, all he answered was one word: No."

The Big Creek ranching families had not raised enough children to qualify for a school under the regulations of those days. You needed ten for openers and eight to stay.

To satisfy the bureaucrats, families temporarily adopted two children from elsewhere—Sonny Haines from Alexis Creek and Hattie Bliss from Redstone. These waifs were returned to their parents after the school authorities had been satisfied that Big Creek had done its share to make the twentieth century Canada's.

"I can't remember what I was paid, but that doesn't matter much anyway if you enjoy your work. Anyway, I was a Depression child with no extravagant tastes. The people were wonderful and the kids were wonderful."

Life presented her with a number of interesting crises in that year.

Charlie Bambrick came screaming into her schoolroom one afternoon with blood pouring from his mouth. He was only five, too young for school, but his age, too, had been faked by his elders so that the school could open, and, having enrolled him, it was decided that he would go anyway.

"He and his sister used to ride an old mare to school and Charlie's father had warned him never to put a cold bit in the horse's mouth. This day it was far, far below zero and Charlie had tried to warm the bit by sticking it in his own mouth and it had frozen to the skin of his tongue."

The stove burned wood. School closed if temperatures were lower than twenty below, Fahrenheit. The children talked corral talk, every second word blue, and they did not entirely see why Elsie thought it was as good to say "Go to Halifax" as "Go to Hell."

"They appreciated school. More then than now, perhaps. But their horizons did not extend beyond Big Creek. They never gave a thought to the possibility of someday working or living in a place that didn't have ranches in it."

In the years since 1946, Elsie taught in other small schools, married, raised her own family, taught some more and, finally, widowed and far more ample of figure than when she left Saskatchewan, she came back to be the Big Creek schoolteacher again.

The school is still one room, but it is a mobile one with propane heat and electric light. The schoolteacher's house next door is another smart, modern mobile home. Elsie drives a Nova and can take herself to Williams Lake, now a big town, in a mere two hours.

The children still travel as much as fourteen miles to classes, but they are driven in station wagons and sedans.

There is an ice rink in the school grounds. The classes see school TV broadcasts.

"It's different now in that the children have limitless horizons. They know there are all sorts of things to do in the world."

Apart from that, she says, kids are kids.

"I have never had a problem getting kids to come to school and I don't have a problem today.

"People talk about so many Indian children being dropouts. Well, I just haven't had the dropouts among them. Some of my Indian pupils win prizes for best attendance.

"One thing I suppose helps, if you remember—Indian people have a great sense of humour and I always try to remember to use humour with Indian children.

"But all kids are kids and they don't change much anywhere. I am of the firm conviction that if you make school a happy experience you will never have problems getting children to learn.

"And the one thing I have never done . . . I don't think . . . I hope I've never done it . . . I never talk down to a child. You never treat a child as your inferior."

The one-room school becomes rarer each year. Busing in most areas carries children of ever-lower ages to large, centralized schools. The Big Creek school, now as before, offers teaching only to the Grade 7 level. Thereafter, Elsie may help youngsters who are taking high school courses by correspondence but must go to Williams Lake and are housed there in the dormitory.

"In the big classes," says Elsie, "there's a tendency for the children to be lost in the crowd."

For herself, she wants nothing but the one-room school which she has. She is marrying again this spring but will, she says, still be the Big Creek schoolmarm and enjoying it as much as in the old log school that stood on Swamp Meadow. Or was it called Mosquito Flats?

The Old Orchardist

KELOWNA—Notice issued by an Okanagan farmer who rents tent space to vacationing families:

1. You are camped in what used to be my orchard. The bugs ate half of it and that thrice-accursed spray program killed the rest. So I have turned it into a camp ground at a dollar a night.

2. I notice that you have brought a lot of canned beer. Please throw these beer cans anywhere that they will make a pattern attractive to your eye. Your own front lawn. Your living room floor. The boulevard outside your house in Vancouver. Or the Queen Elizabeth Theater Plaza. I ask you to make only one exception. Don't throw them around here.

3. I am almost as old as Woodward's Stores. But I am not as well stocked. I do not have for sale a carton of salt, white gas, or a spare Buick axle-housing.

4. For the same reason that I am just a 72-year-old, tired, retired fruit farmer, please do not ask me to fix your gas stove. I could never fix my own when I was younger.

5. You may, of course, find me pawing around the innards of my old LaSalle or perhaps trying to fix the gate hinges. I earnestly request you, do not offer to help me. The last camper who insisted on helping me fused the entire switch-box on my house. I cannot afford to accept free help.

6. I do not sell worms for fishing.

7. I did not ride the Wells Fargo stages and I did not come to

Canada just ahead of a posse. My father was a greengrocer in Chatham, Ontario, and I belong to the Rotary Club.

8. I do not know how much my neighbour is asking for that piece of land.

9. The story of your recent operation is very interesting, ma'am, but I have had three of my own.

10. The same goes for children.

11. I do not have a four-cent stamp.

12. Beyond the camp ground, behind those signs marked "No Trespassing," "Keep Out," and "Private Property," there is a patch of poison ivy. I can only advise you to wash well and quickly in soap and water immediately after contact.

13. The wind does not always blow like this, but it often blows like this.

14. I do not have a left-handed exhaust-bearing socket wrench and I do not wish to sell the front gates.

15. Your Esso Credit Card is no good here, and I do not have a supply of counter cheques.

16. In the winter, I just tough it out somehow, that's all.

17. Do you have anything smaller than a fifty?

Coon

NORTH VANCOUVER—The coon who lives in our yard is probably no smarter than any other coons. But he thinks a lot. It is one of the advantages of living on a dead-end street. Very few cars come up Cardiac Climb to our house, and the forest which begins at the edge of the lawn extends all the way to Lillooet. This situation makes for quiet, meditative coons.

Our coon lives under the little woodshed that collapsed in last December's snow. Being a good tenant he is left alone. He is quiet. No wild parties. He contributes nothing to the prosperity of the household, but at least he is not a sponger. We leave no food for him and he earns his own living doing some kind of work in the neighbours' chicken houses. It is a night job and he sleeps all day, so sometimes months pass during which we never set eyes on one another.

Last night, we met for the first time since February. It was just after the national news on Channel 2. Earl Cameron, that pleasant chap with the reverse dimple in his chin, had just brought us all the news of fresh disasters and had been followed by someone who gave penetrating insight into the utter hopelessness of the situation in Viet Nam, the population explosion, and the stock market. Obviously, we'd be ludicrously optimistic in starting another batch of dill pickles. In fact, it seemed scarcely worth a man's time to go to bed for another night, and a walk on the lawn seemed as good a way of going as any.

There was dew on the grass, and when the house lights rushed out the open door, they quickly manufactured millions of small rubies there. The mountain had released the cool air from the top of her head and was allowing it to flow down her sides, like the long hair of a beautiful woman preparing for bed. There is a large fir tree, down where the weeds have almost completely obliterated the red fescue and creeping bent.

The coon burst out of this cover as I came near and flung himself on the trunk of the tree. He went up it like a high rigger, throwing his forearms out to catch the safety belt that he doesn't really have, digging the sharp little claws of his hind legs into the grey bark like a set of climbing irons. Then he paused, his forearms resting across the third branch, and looked down at me.

The black mask he wears across his eyes is neater than most, shaped very distinctly. Remember elegant Leslie Howard playing the Scarlet Pimpernel in movies long ago, holding that black mask to his eyes in the Paris ballroom scenes? Leslie Howard is dead, of course, shot down by the Germans in an airliner out of Portugal during the last war. The Germans apparently believed that Sir Winston Churchill was on the plane. It was a case of mistaken intelligence.

What has the death of one movie actor got to do with all this anyway, or the starvation of 10,000 people on the streets of Calcutta? What connection with a coon and me in Lynn Valley, where an orange moon is showing through the branches of the fir tree?

"Coon," I said, "something bloody awful has happened to this world that we seemed to have planned so well twenty-five years ago."

He thought about this and then started down the tree trunk on the opposite side, pausing now and then and poking his face around the trunk to look at me. He seemed to think I was angry about something, but why be angry about anything. Isn't the world up to quota in anger tonight?

Instead of running away when he reached the ground, he walked, stiff-legged, to the bottomless black shadow which had collected beneath the rhododendron bush.

"You're a bit of a fraud, Coon," I said. "You think all day about the affairs of the world, up there in the old woodshed. But what do you do about it? You delude yourself that it is enough to think."

He walked toward me a step or two, into the moonlight which had now forced its way through the fir branches and splashed on the lawn. How small his hands, and how thin his wrists.

"True, true," I said. "We should have arranged the world better for you, Coon. I am not only larger than you, but also smarter. And you are a tenant of mine. My responsibility is far greater than yours."

The air coming down the mountain rustled the jagged leaves of the Oregon grape on the ground beside us and pushed a cloud across the moon above. With as much dignity as he could manage, Coon walked past me—so close that I might have snatched the topmost ring of his tail. And then the shadows beyond the lawn's edge covered him completely, and I was left alone. Even more alone than before.

Frontier Justice
at Cut Rates

VANCOUVER—The name of the community in which this incident occurred is hiding in a dark corner beneath my desk. When I put my hand there it growls and snaps. Let us leave it there.

It was a frontier town of this dynamic land. The mayor was a young man, intent on doing right. On the morning that I met him, he found himself faced with the duty of acting as judge. Mayors are all magistrates and when sickness or other cause removes regular magistrates from the courts, mayors may be obliged to serve in their stead, even if they know no more law than a new-laid egg. I accompanied His Worship to the courtroom.

Only one guest had occupied Hotel Crowbar overnight. He stood, sock-footed, before the bench while the charge was read to him. He was charged with being in a state of intoxication in a public place. He pleaded guilty to indigestion.

A young Mountie supplied the details, speaking in unemotional tones. Accused had flagged down the town's lone RCMP patrol car at midnight. Accused had entered car and demanded that he be driven to a nice quiet hotel. Accused had seemed surprised on being informed that he was not in a taxi. Accused had apologized and left, but the graciousness of his departure had been marred by the fact that he fell like an over-age pine tree and lay unmoving in the ditch. The law had then gathered him up.

The mayor asked if the prisoner could afford a $10 fine. A sensible question. One wonders why it isn't asked more often in the Assizes. On being assured that the prisoner was stakey, the mayor imposed a $10 fine and $2.50 in costs.

It seemed a simple matter. But later, while we were exclaiming on the efficiency of the town's new water system, His Worship confided that he found occasions such as those unnerving. If they occurred frequently during his term of office, he intended to go back to accounting.

Later that day, after an examination of the sewage plant and other community art works, I returned alone to the hotel bar. There was the prisoner of the morning, deep in the zinfandel again.

"I've seen you before somewhere," he said. "You a policeman?"

I said I was a newspaperman. He was delighted and pressed upon me the full details of name, age, and address of next-of-kin in Edmonton. I judged that he hoped a newspaper report of his being jailed would serve instead of a letter to assure the dear ones that he was alive and happy.

Those details are now lost in a windrow of white notes which have drifted in one corner of the basement. I recall that his name was Italian and that he answered to the name Dutchie. He was one of a group of technicians engaged in reballasting the Canadian National Railway line and was himself the operator of a Mexican drag line—which is what you and I usually call a shovel.

"That was a pretty good magistrate," said Dutchie.

"That was no magistrate," I said. "That was the mayor."

"She's quite a town," observed Dutchie. "The Mounties run the taxis and the mayor runs the law. Well, anyhow, he's a nice fellow."

"You liked the sentence?"

"Like it? A real bargain. Here I was last night, with indigestion. If I'd been able to digest all that booze I would have been okay, wouldn't I? So it was indigestion.

"The bar is closed. This hotel is full. I'm looking for a hotel room, and in this town you can't get anything for under eight bucks. If I get a taxi he's probably going to charge me four bucks and I'll probably tip him a two spot. That's fourteen, not counting breakfast at one-fifty, supposing I can eat it. Fifteen to sixteen dollars.

"The way things worked out, the taxi is free. I get a good room, clean, warm, for ten. The fluff only charge me two-and-a-half for looking after my wallet and serving me breakfast, which is so good I do eat some of it. It's quiet. There's time for a long sleep. Check-out time isn't until 10:30. And when I have to cash a pay cheque to pay the fine, they drive me back downtown free to do that.

"Nice town," said Dutchie, "nice people here."

The Sidehill Gouger Situation

VANCOUVER—We have some new and exciting information today about two little-known B.C. wildlife species, the Cariboo alligator and the sidehill gouger. For this, we are in the debt of two men who make an avocation of natural history. They have gone out in the field, where earnest researchers should be, and they have used their powers of observation well. They have been active while too many of the rest of us, I fear, have been sitting around in PTA committee meetings, raking leaves, chopping firewood, and engaging in other vulgar and futile pursuits. Our first report is from Norman Shaw of Powell River:

> Some time ago, in one of your columns in *The Sun,* I noted a reference to that curious and engaging animal, the sidehill gouger *(Lopsidium sardonicus).* May I offer the following observations which were made in the Ashnola district of the Similkameen country.
>
> Sidehill gougers were once plentiful on those hills, although I fear they are now nearing extinction. A great loss to all lovers of nature. Originally, all the gougers of this area were of the right-hand variety. That is, both of the right legs were longer than the left, and they were therefore compelled to graze the mountains in a counterclockwise direction. In the early twenties, however, a number of left-hand sidehill gougers appeared.
>
> When two of the same sex but of opposite type met on a mountainside a fierce battle would ensue. The loser, in the agony of defeat, would momentarily forget its natural limitations, turn tail to flee and inevitably fall to its death. If the meeting were between opposite sexes, the result was equally unfortunate, although more interesting. The animals would attempt to mate, but would almost always die of frustration and exhaustion.

Occasionally, by the exercise of the utmost perseverance and ingenuity, equalled in the animal kingdom only by the porcupine, a union would be consummated. The offspring were uniformly unfortunate.

The hybrids were of three types. One was the *high-behinded* sidehill gouger. It could only travel uphill and invariably died of starvation on the top of the mountain on which it was born. All the higher peaks of the Ashnola contain a few pitiful heaps of their bones. The *low-behinded* sidehill gouger was once considered a separate species *(Lopsidium sauras)*. Its fate was similar to that of the high-behinded variety. As for the third type, *corner-high*, these unfortunates couldn't move anywhere. The devoted parents would attempt to bring food to the young, but since they had to make a complete circuit of the mountain for every feeding, starvation naturally ensued.

We can only be grateful that at least in the remote vastness of the Cariboo country, the haunting calls of the gougers may still be heard. For how long, one wonders.

One does wonder. But, on to more cheerful information. There is evidence that the Cariboo alligator *(Alligator caigator impulsivus)* has not only retained some territory in the Cariboo, but has also spread to the western coast of Vancouver Island. The report is from Jules Cariou of Port Alice on the west coast of Vancouver Island. He writes:

Am shipping by separate container a specimen of your famous Cariboo alligator, found by myself in the Rumble Beach area. This specimen was bagged November 2 in the morning, before the sun had crossed the yardarm.

I was hunting by myself, with a 300 Savage, when I came upon the alligator near a washed-out bridge—the only kind of bridge we have in this country. The creature was unmistakable. The colouring was right—dark scaly top-hide, golden red belly, beady black eyes, and long in the tooth and claw. I did not shoot him. He was dying when I found him.

I laid the 300 Savage on the ground and walked up beside him. Then I sat down to think about it. I lit my pipe and smoked it upside down (so I wouldn't drown) and thought a long time.

I can't say that it was a very pleasant time, me gurgling on the pipe and the alligator approaching the climax of his biography with considerable rolling of the eyes. And the wind was cold and sharp as a Wilkinson blade after the thirteenth shave. I will not remember this as one of my favourite occasions.

After a while, the alligator expired. I made a yoke of the 300 Savage and dragged him home. I am sure you will know where to stuff him.

Spring Breakup

ALEXIS CREEK—All who love dirt roads and cheap whisky will want to note the most thrilling festival of the British Columbia interior which is called Spring Breakup. There is nothing in our cities to compare with it.

There are participants of the Spring Breakup jamboree kneeling beside the festival shrine—the boghole—stuffing wood under spinning truck wheels, soaking their suits in mud, and calling loudly upon their Maker in tones of deep emotion.

Nature arranges few things for men more colourful, invigorating, and exciting than breakup.

Breakup takes a lot of preparation which Nature, in her methodical manner, does all through the long winters in the Cariboo, the Chilcotin, the Peace—anywhere that there are people to be inconvenienced.

Through winter's freezes and thaws, ice crystals form in the beds of roads. Sometimes they form a great lens of ice which remains invisible to the motorist as he speeds over it in those frozen months when the road surface may be as hard and smooth as pavement.

Then comes the thaw, and sometimes rain with it and, where once was road, there remains naught but a dismal tarn ripped by ruts two feet deep and filled with brown water rimmed with shell ice.

These bogholes appear in low sections of the road or where culverts have plugged. They also appear in high sections of the road where no culverts have plugged. Nature works in mysterious ways.

They have a custom of appearing, year after year, in the same section of road. This is handy for the highways people because they can tell, year after year, which sections of the road will cause complaint. They are thereby protected from unsettling surprises.

One boghole of memory in Chilcotin was one mile long and ran straight and true between rows of black jackpine beside some little lakes named the Crazy Lakes.

The local residents were wont to petition for culverts and for gravelling. After a few years they petitioned for a bridge or, failing that, ferry boats.

The government eventually rebuilt this road and the locals have had to take their complaints elsewhere, but this was, in a way, a pity, for that boghole was suited for a national shrine to the muffler and tailpipe industry.

I am no expert on bogholes, having never been stuck for longer than twelve consecutive hours in any one hole. Also my experience is intermittent. I haven't been bogged down since the day before yesterday at North Bend in the Fraser Canyon and it may not happen again for weeks. Some people get stuck every day at this time of year.

What can one do about bogholes?

Short of staying home, a cowardly course which our highways department recommends, one should pack a shovel, hip waders, chains, ropes and pulleys, an axe, a truck jack, food, tent, sleeping bag, and the Bible.

As you approach the boghole stop and look at it.

Awful, isn't it?

There are chunks of wood floating in the puddles which appear to be the wreckage of rafts on which some poor wretches have tried to make it to shore. They aren't rafts. Wayfarers before you have jacked up the back wheels, poked boughs and logs underneath, and, because they were lazy and laid the wood lengthwise, slipped off and bedded their car even deeper.

They should have laid the wood crossways for a corduroy road, as did their ancestors. Then twenty or thirty vehicles might have crossed this stretch before the corduroy sticks broke up, snatched off the muffler, and released the full-throated roar of the engine to the spring air.

Now having looked at the boghole and thought these thoughts, you should put on the waders and walk into the thing, testing for bottom which is there somewhere. In the overlay you will frequently discover big sharp rocks which can punch a hole in your oil pan and a bit of blood where the careless folk have cut themselves on ice or tire chains.

In the most famous of Chilcotin bogholes the mud has a rare consistency, and natives call it the Fragrant Guano of the Great Northern Loon, Sweet Songstress of the Lonely Lakes, although they usually shorten the title.

By choosing your best rut, by rearranging any rocks, lunch pails, shovel heads, or other things you may find that won't float away, by chaining up the car before you get into trouble, you may make it to the other side where the road is merely sloppy and miserable.

Will you do that?

Of course not.

You will charge in. Halfway through the car will slow, give a gentle sigh, and come to rest high-centred and immoveable.

Now you know why you brought the Bible.

Watching the Bankers Break Cover

Next to watching prairie chicken being flushed from thick cover by a good dog, I enjoy watching a bunch of startled Canadian bankers.

Bankers, like the sharp-tailed grouse, grow plump if allowed to do exactly what they have always done without being asked to fly. They prefer to stay in thick cover and out of sight and take their sustenance a grain at a time, chuckling quietly to themselves about how it all adds up.

Now and then some intruder enters this domain. Then the first instinct of the species is to remain perfectly still and trust it won't be noticed.

The decision to go to the air is invariably taken in panic. Clucking wildly, they lumber into the sky and fly a course so predictably straight that they are sometimes in danger of dashing their brains out on slow-moving trees.

Canadian bankers broke cover this week because of the actions of some American bankers, a breed they consider scarcely worthy of the name. American bankers are, to the Canadian types, flirty creatures with money and sometimes, like artists, prostitutes, and newspapermen, a threat to the very underpinnings of our Western civilization.

If you would know the latest offence against good banking practice in the U.S., it is that banks have been offering loans at cut rates.

This was started a year ago by People's National Bank of Maryland. It conducted a three-month sale, lending money at 7.5 per cent for twelve months and 8.5 per cent for thirty-six months. The usual rate is 10 per cent.

This outrage no doubt caused some stirrings and a few quiet clucks in the Canadian banking community, but our men decided to lie low and trust Divine Providence to bring the Yanks back to sanity.

This year, two more American banks took up the idea.

American Security Bank of Washington cut its loan rate to 8 per cent from 11.5 per cent for one day. Five thousand borrowers applied, 2500 got loans, and the bank's volume of loans went up to $8 million in that twenty-four-hour period.

First Virginia Bank, also of Washington, held a seven-week sale of money, offering it at a 10-per-cent reduction of ordinary interest rates. It, too, did much business.

To you and me, these sales may seem less than an excuse to call out the militia.

Banks don't make money by taking $10 and $20 deposits from you and me and keeping them in savings accounts. A banker who had all savers and no borrowers would very quickly find it advisable to go back to the farm before Dad changed his will.

The business of banks is to lend our money to other people for a higher interest rate than they pay us. The man with the savings account is not a bank customer, he is a partner in the enterprise; he hopes that the bank's management will be able to lend his money at rates which will profit both him and the bank.

The true customer of a bank is the man who comes to borrow money.

The entire banking business depends upon his patronage.

He is, or should be, in the catbird seat, free to shop among fiercely competing lenders and choosing to give his custom only to those whose rates and service are to his taste. Only by some legerdemain has the Canadian banking system contrived to give the impression that depositors are its customers and that borrowers are feckless people who wouldn't need loans if they managed their business as well as bankers do.

If a chain grocery, a hardware store, or a car wash holds a sale, we customers assume that the firms are taking less profit on each transaction, but expect to make up the difference by increased volume. Or, that they are overstocked and prepared to sell some items at cost or a trifle below to solicit new customers from whom profits may be made in future.

This makes the reaction of the Royal Bank of Canada spokesman so apt—all fuss and feathers.

"I am not satisfied that banks, as pillars of society, should become discount houses," he said. ("I am a pillar of society," clucks the prairie chicken while the spaniel thrashes around in her clover patch.)

Further, said the Royal's anonymous old hen, "our shareholders might not look kindly upon a cut-rate establishment." I doubt that, too. Shareholders look at annual dividends, not at the individual transactions by which they were generated. Do Army and Navy Department Store shareholders complain when their store knocks 33 per cent off the list price of underwear?

As an occasional borrower from Canadian banks, I wish them all to know that I shall not think less of them if they offer loans at cut-rate interest.

Silent Ken

BIG CREEK—When I suggested to Kenny Skomoroh that we take a couple of horses and try to pick up a moose, it was below freezing and wind was driving snow horizontal to the ground.

"Okay," he said.

I discussed the weather and the behaviour of moose at such times. Would they be in the timber or in the meadows? Would they be spooky? In short, were we likely to get a shot, all things considered?

"Maybe," he said.

We left the ranch at first light in a Merc one-ton truck that should have gone long ago to the Great Car Lot in The Sky. Half an hour later, we got stuck.

"Damn," said Kenny.

He worked us loose. We went on and stuck again.

"Hell," he said.

The third time we stuck he didn't offer any comment.

He spun the wheels. He shovelled. He spun some more. He unslung the chains, got out the jack, fixed the jack, jacked the jack, bruised his hands, haywired the chains, plied the pliers, and used a screw-driver for a chisel, with slush down his neck and mud on his face and the truck and two horses threatening to topple on him from the rickety jack and end it all.

Like other men of the country, he has the skill, the patience, and the endurance to take that old truck up a mountain and load it with glacier ice or fly it to the sky and snatch golden apples from the sun, once his mind be made up to it.

He got the chains on and raced the motor.

One chain came loose and whistled away over a meadow.

"Bastard," said Kenny.

He was up to two syllables.

He took off the chain and rocked the truck out, drove two more miles, backed the truck against a snowdrift to unload the horses off the tailgate and it stuck again.

I asked if this meant we would have to try chaining up again when we rode back here in the dark.

"Probably," he said.

Then I asked him which horse was mine.

"The brown," he said.

That shows, once again, that most people talk more than is necessary.

If I'd waited until he got aboard his pinto, it would have been made quite clear to me that I was riding the brown and there wouldn't have been all that talk.

After that I left conversation to Kenny.

Four hours later he talked some more. He stopped his horse, got off, tied it, and started building a fire.

"Dinner time," he said.

Later that day he pointed at a few poles on the edge of a meadow.

"Camped there once."

I pointed to a squared poplar post. "There's something written there," I said.

"Franklin," he said.

If I knew who or what Franklin was, he needn't say more. If I needed to know more, I could ask. The system works very well.

I did not ask.

Late in the afernoon I said I reckoned we had cut the tracks of three moose.

"I'd say four," he said.

We didn't keep that argument going any longer.

Sometimes we walked to get warm. On the horses we sat, feet frozen in the stirrups, hunched over, looking at the saddle horn as if there was an important message written on it.

He spoke five times to his horse. Three times he said, "Huhu, huhu." The other times he called it a knothead and a son of a bitch.

When the day was old and the sky was colouring, he stopped his pinto and held up one hand. Then pointed to a moose in the jackpines. Only bulls are legal.

"Cow," he said.

There wasn't anything more to say on that subject, so we rode back to the truck, fought mud, snow, chains, and sulky cayuses and got back to the ranch deep in the darkness. They asked what kind of a day we had had.

"Cold," said Kenny.

The rancher from whom I borrowed the horse wouldn't take payment but he said it would be fair enough to pay Ken a Class B Guide's rate for the day. I mailed Ken a cheque from Vancouver. It was almost the next summer before I ran into him again.

"You never cashed that cheque I sent you, Ken."

"Nope."

"You got it all right?"

"Yep."

"Ken, why didn't you cash the cheque?"

"Ain't needed it yet," said Ken.

The Caribou Hunt

I'm truly sorry man's dominion
Has broken nature's social union
And justifies thy ill opinion of me,
Thy poor earth-born companion
And fellow mortal.
   —Rabbie Burns in Ode to a Field Mouse.

ATLIN—The caribou was a dry cow with thin short antlers still in the velvet. She was grazing alone among pearl-grey rocks on a grey morning in the high country above Atlin when I came upon her from above.

She was the first caribou I had seen that day and the odds are that I was the first human she was ever to see. She was a mite careless, for she had not heard me come over the rise, and now, when I was silhouetted against the clouds, her eye didn't catch me. She would graze on the few wisps of grass or weed which were laced thinly among the rocks here, far above timberline.

Now and then she would raise her head and look right and left, unhurried, taken with the unconciousness and ease of a human wiping his mouth with a table napkin.

For the fun of it I stalked her. There was little else to do. We two had the mountain all to ourselves that morning.

When she dropped her head to feed I pulled myself forward on my elbows with the gun strapped on my back. When she raised her head I froze with the flap of a big grey wool sweater flopped over my face and did my best to resemble a rock.

Once or twice she looked directly at me but she didn't catch a movement. I was within one hundred yards before her ears came forward and there was that almost indetectable tightening of the body, the first stage of awareness and alarm.

Enough foolishness on this cold barren hill where shell ice winked in the pools among the heather and foxberry. I peeled off the rifle, put it beside me and sat on a frosty rock to watch her run.

She stood a long time, then took a few steps toward me.

Their eyes aren't good. It is hard for us to know exactly what shapes and forms they do see in their world of black, grey, and white.

She could probably see that my shape wasn't that of a wolf. There are no cougar this far north. If I were a bear she could easily outrun me from a hundred-yard start but that, perhaps, is what she thought I was.

One step at a time she advanced, ten, twenty, thirty feet, moving sometimes from side to side, lifting a wet nose to taste the wind. What breeze there was came from her to me. In the last century commercial hunters on the prairies attracted curious antelope within gunshot by waving a flag.

I raised my arm, not too abruptly, and slowly waved it from side to side. She came to within fifty yards; it was time for conversation.

Not kitcheekoo sounds; animals don't like to be talked down to. They can hear condescension in your voice. I spoke to her as to anyone else.

"You notice this rifle, old cow?" I said. "That is one of the safest bets on this mountain for you. As you can see, it's a converted U.S. Army P14.

"Since it was made for an army, they made it clubby and ugly. They would go to extra expense to prevent it being graceful.

"Also, since it was made by contractors for soldiers whose lives would depend on its reliability, it frequently misfires and jams."

Her nostrils moved. She made no sound, but she was sympathetic to any ideas, however new.

"One thing you haven't seen before," I said, "is a grizzly bear who smokes cigars." Deliberately I pulled my last from the shirt pocket and lit it.

The scent reached her. She whirled, stumbled, almost fell, then hit the long caribou pace and angled right up a draw where small flat rocks rang like ceramic bells under her feet.

She paused once at the crest to look back and then winked out of sight.

I am sorry I embarrassed that old cow. I had, in a sense, made fun of her, and it was her mountain, not mine. I enjoyed the cigar.

How Paddy and Grasshopper Blew the Bridge

A great big box of dynamite
and a hundred feet of fuse,
a little box of blasting caps
and a belly full of booze
This is the fine condition
I was in the other night,
When I scared hell out of half the town
doing what I thought was right.
Note found in the Fort Nelson RCMP lock-up, March, 1961

FORT NELSON—In daylight hours the contortions of the ionosphere are such that only one radio station may be heard here, and sometimes it is faint.

One day in February, 1961, when Krushchev announced that he intended to smash the United Nations, Fort Nelson heard it as a declaration of war on the United States. And as the Moccasin Telegraph spread the news through the bush, it became known that the Russian armored divisions were already moving.

Two catskinners—one named Paddy, the other called Grasshopper—were the first Canadians to flock to the colours in the new war. They had been drinking at the time, but not so much that they failed to perceive that the Alaska Highway was a dagger pointed at the heart of Washington.

This being the case, what better and prompter service to the Allied cause than to blow the bridge across the Muskwa, three miles south of town?

They obtained a fifty-pound case of forty per cent Forcite from Explosives Limited, charging it to an employer who had recently fired them.

However, they had no transport. Paddy and Grasshopper were not men to drive while they were drinking. So, carrying the case of dynamite, the fuse, and the blasting caps, they moved among the citizenry of Fort Nelson, beseeching men to drive them to the Muskwa River.

For it was necessary to blow the bridge there, to blow it cleanly and finely with the spruce needles raining down from that sky which is so very clear and high above the Muskwa because they were for the Republic.

Ernest Hemingway seems to be getting into this copy. Let us run through that sentence again: They tried to get somebody to drive them out to the bridge.

It was one of those tactical failures which are the despair of all great generals. Some men of Fort Nelson said yes, they would drive them to the bridge, but later. Some at the Fort Nelson Hotel insisted on finishing their beer first. Others suggested that the bridge be left open to enable the American troops to move north against the Russians. Several urged Paddy and Grasshopper to give up cigarettes.

They never reached the bridge. It is still there. Late in the day, RCMP constables Orichowski and Dandy gathered up the two guerillas, the dynamite, the fuse, and the caps and placed them in the custody of Her Majesty. Paddy and Grasshopper were fined $500 each, and have since departed this region.

But the record of Canada's first confrontation with Khrushchev, long before Mr. Kennedy did the same thing in Cuba, remains now in the lines of the jailhouse ballad:

> Now it seems the bloody Russians
> was coming down the road,
> I says "Stop them at the Liard Bridge."
> He says "Stop them at the Toad."
> We will stop them any handy place,
> on any hill or ridge,
> we had better pull the rag out
> and blow the Muskwa Bridge.

But I want you people all to know
that I'm not a drunken clown,
and I don't give two hoots in hell
if the Russians take this town.

A Depressing View
from Cardiac Climb

VANCOUVER—The Cardiac Climb Men's Protective Association, one of the smaller of B.C.'s traditional folk moots, held a short and subdued meeting recently amid the smoke of burning leaves.

The chairman noted that autumn is a melancholy season and that man is born to trouble as the sparks fly upward. But the general membership should remember, he said, that man's destiny is sublime and that we do ever move onward and upward, stepping on the dead selves of our former things. The meeting decided, by unanimous vote, that the chairman didn't have the faintest idea of what he was talking about. He was voted out of office and refused cigarette makings.

The new chairman promised to establish a more responsible tone in society debates. He suggested as a theme for the Christmas season: "Things are far worse than any of us realize." This was adopted; ayes 8, nays 0, one abstaining.

The new federal mini-budget was discussed. Four members participating in the debate took the view that the tax increase was too small, that the threatened deficit was too large, and that disaster lay ahead. This was contested hotly by four other speakers who maintained that the tax increase was too large, that it would depress the nation's economy, and that disaster lay ahead. In order to effect unanimity, a motion was put forward that the federal government be condemned for inviting disaster by unwise budgetary policy. This carried 8 to 0, one member abstaining.

The former chairman of the society, who had abstained from two previous votes, then told a funny story about a fishing trip. The membership agreed that it was undersize and threw it back.

The hazards of famine were discussed. It was noted that the world population is increasing at the rate of 167,000 a year, while the increase in food supply is only one percent in the underdeveloped countries. The matter was referred to committee for study.

Other items of general hazard discussed included the Berlin issue, the Cuban issue, and the fact that drivers caught using metal-studded snow tires in the state of Georgia may be sentenced to one month in county public work camps.

The retired chairman said that the Dr. Zhivago theme song was a pleasant melody. This was discussed on the usual high plane of formal debate in the Men's Protective Association. It was decided, by a vote of 8 to 1, that the Dr. Zhivago theme song sounded like an old electric mixer starting up.

A member devoted to the pursuit of arcane statistics noted that over half of twenty-three million stock-holders of the United States were women and that more than half of these were housewives. This, he said, boded ill for Canada's greatest trading partner. In addition, it had given his wife a brand new idea which she had not possessed on Saturday of last week. The member was thanked for his timely remarks.

Productivity in Canada was discussed, and all sang one of the favourite club songs:

> Those who work
> and do their best
> go down the road
> like all the rest.

The former chairman asked leave to address a series of questions to the membership. This was granted. Was it or was it not true, he wanted to know, that no member of the association had failed to keep up his mortgage payments in the year past, that none had gone to hospital, or, if they had, were not better for it, and that not one was currently in jail or Toronto?

Was there any member present, he asked, who had not in the year past bought a fishing rod, a TV, or some other article which gave him pleasure? Was there any member who had not in that time seen a good football game, scored low on golf or high in bowling, eaten a good meal in Chinatown, found a rare book, or made something for his house of which he was proud?

Unfortunately, before he could complete his questioning, time expired. Two members of the association were found by their wives, four others were located by platoons of children sent on scouting expeditions by wives and there were tasks enough for all. Lacking a quorum, the meeting adjourned without formal motion, pursuant to standing orders made and provided. The former chairman was left alone with his leaf pile, which burned very slowly in the dank November air.

The Death of Lester

ANAHIM LAKE—Saturday afternoon around two o'clock, Lester Dorsey will finally keep an appointment on time. He will be buried in the Anahim cemetery.

He will be cast into that pale brown rocky ground beside his wife, Mickey, who was buried just a month ago. She was the sixth and he will be the seventh white buried there. It is yet new country. Until the day before yesterday, it was frontier.

We are lucky, those of us who were privileged to know such people—Lester, Mickey, Rich Hobson, who wrote *Grass Beyond the Mountains* and died, and Pan Phillips, who is among the last of the old originals, and lives.

These people were obscure. They lived an obscure life in a small and inconsequential place. As chance had it, for reasons you and I will never know, they were also great people. They were larger than life. Heroic is the word.

Of Mickey, the wife, it is perhaps too late to speak adequately, except to say that she was the most heroic of them all, because she was a ranch wife. Ranch wives have to be observed to be believed. They are the greatest and the most unnoticed of all the great Canadians.

I find it easier to write of Lester. He was male and foolish, like me.

So his funeral on that dusty little sidehill next to the stampede grounds at Anahim Lake will be a huge affair, by the standards of that sparsely settled land. Big men of high reputation in this world will be there, and so will raggedy-ass small ranchers who dwell on the fringes of the settled world, men who have worked hard and as well as Lester did but who were less noticeable because they lacked a certain magic. Lester had the magic.

What was the magic? I'm not sure.

To know Lester was to be constantly amazed by his fortitude, charmed by his languid grace, exasperated by his stubborn refusal to admit that clocks or calendars existed for the purpose of appointments, shocked by his failure to comprehend what a dollar was or what security meant, and, finally, entranced by his stories.

It was a combination of all those qualities, spread across two yards of lean and agile human male, that established Lester as the central point of any gathering. It didn't matter what the meeting was called for—Lester was the man you noticed.

It wasn't his position. He was not sure what that word meant. It wasn't wealth. He never had wealth. He was a good drinker, he could braid horsehair, and he could tell stories, but when it came to making money he never quite found the trick of it.

A good part of another generation will be spent in Chilcotin sorting out all the memories about the great Lester Dorsey.

For me, who will also be sorting for some years, the most recent memory will be easiest. He told me a new grizzly bear story. I thought I'd heard them all. By some chance I had missed this one.

All Lester's stories were masterpieces of the art of story-telling. Each was vivid. It was exciting. And there was a kink in the tail.

The story was that he had gone late of a morning to wrangle horses in one of his many hunting camps in the Rainbow Mountains, a halter in one hand, unarmed, and unprepared for the big grizzly that reared up out of a dry creek bed and stood puffing its breath into his face.

"Running was no way out," he said, "and I couldn't walk past him as if I hadn't noticed him. I did the only thing I could think of. I cursed him. I didn't raise my voice, but I cursed him. I used every dirty, foul word I had ever heard in my life.

"It was something to see that bear. He danced on one foot and he danced on the other foot. He shifted back and forth and he waved his arms. You could see that that bear had never heard language like that in his life before.

"After a while, the bear got down on four legs again and walked away.

"Lucky for me that bear had such delicate feelings.

For a man with a reputation for being a bit on the wild side, Lester himself had some delicate ways. One was not swearing when women were present. A lot of the time he didn't remember it, but he remembered the rule more than most men.

Among either men or women his voice was typically soft and faintly accented from the American Southlands, where courtesy is everything that matters.

In the first of the several heart attacks that finally killed him, he went to Williams Lake Memorial Hospital, where there were such things unlovely to him as half-shell nighties and bedpans. The speculation among his friends was intense. How long would Lester stick those conditions? To the surprise of all he lasted to the day the doctors told him he could go.

It was his wife Mickey who revealed the secret. "When they put him in bed I snatched all his clothes and took them home with me. Lester is extremely modest, you know."

I remember another occasion when he was not so easily corralled.

He had come to Vancouver General Hospital to have his gall bladder removed. He refused to remain more than a few days because, he explained, he would miss the annual fall meeting of the Anahim Lake Cattlemen's Association. Next to stampede, that is the major social event of the year.

Reluctantly, the doctor freed him from Vancouver General on the promise that he would touch nothing with fat in it for many weeks. I drove him to Anahim on a trip that involved much pain for him, he having eaten largely on fish and chips, a dish for which he had conceived a sudden passion.

It was cold that winter. The thermometer hit 55 below when we paused at Puntzi, where Mickey was then teaching school. Next morning the car's clutch shattered like rock candy.

So we missed the cattlemen's meeting, but two days later his aching guts did not deter him from joining me on a moose hunt. He caught a couple of horses, spilling out of his shirt pocket many $10 and $20 bills that had been left for him at Baxter's store by a party of hunters. I collected the money as he moved. He didn't notice much. As I say, he had very little interest in money; I am not sure he ever fully understood what it is supposed to be for.

On that day—ten, eleven, or twelve days after he had lost a fairly valuable part of his body—we rode across those lonely ranges to Gene Mooney's place.

The temperature was still well below zero Fahrenheit. Every twenty minutes or half an hour we had to stop, make a fire, and put our booted feet into it. I remember that he wore jeans, a bitty sheepskin vest, a denim jacket, and on his head an unlined nylon parka hood he had snatched from a peg on the wall of his cabin. Why his ears and most of the rest of him didn't freeze, I have no way of knowing.

"It's never bad when you got a horse to carry you home," he said. "There was a time when a horse dumped me in weather like this, 'way north, on the trail to Rich Hobson's place at Batnuni."

He had been wearing no adequate clothing, having been seized suddenly and without warning of the notion to ride across much of the British Columbia map to visit old Rich. Neither did he have matches, for reasons only God might understand. All that bitter night he kept moving, walking a while, running a while.

"I was pretty near finished when I finally hit a cabin where there was two old trappers.

"I went up and knocked at their door. 'Good morning,' I said, 'I wonder if you could direct me to Rich Hobson's place.'

"They were set back by my looks. I guess I was pretty white. But they pointed down the trail. I said 'Thank you kindly' and turned and started away. But then I fainted and fell down in the snow and they hauled me into the cabin and thawed me out."

The memories crowd in on you.

You say to yourself, how did he live so long? How did he breathe so easy and talk so gentle? What manner of man was this? How did he come about? Is he the last strain? Did they break the mould after they made this one?

As to biography, he came here from Washington state, where he'd been born someplace, not exactly determined, in the Grand Coulee country. He came to Anahim Lake trying to put as much wilderness between himself and the law as possible.

Lester had been fooling around at a country fair, making a

horse that was only half-broke rear. The horse's front feet came down on a quieter citizen's head and broke it. Lester fled north and west in his eighteenth year. It was years later that he met a man from his home country who told him, "Lester, you are runnin' from nothin'. The bugger got up and walked away."

There were, at that time in the early twenties, no roads to Anahim.

Lester packed for the company of gentlemen adventurers we call Hudson's Bay, leading his horse train up and down the Precipice Trail between Bella Coola and Anahim Lake.

He cowboyed here and there. He drank the popular beverage of the country. It was called Peaches Wine and was matured behind the stove in a bucket.

He frequently went hunting.

He fell in love with the high country, the land above timbering. Or, as it is sometimes known, the Hills With the Crust on Top.

He never lost that love. He was happiest on the alpine meadows. He loved that country when riding alone. He loved it when he guided hunters there for caribou. He loved it when, in later years, he learned to use a snowmobile.

The snowmobile was the solitary piece of machinery, out of all the inventions of modern man, to which Lester displayed common decency—even, at times, affection. All the other machines of the modern age he abused. If maltreatment of tractors, trucks, and other engineering masterpieces was ground for fines and imprisonment, they would have had to hang Lester.

In his passion for getting above timberline by horse or, in winter, by snowmobile he missed only one great ambition.

Like most men who hunt a lot, he got tired of gunfire but became enamoured of photography. His private ambition was to guide a party of National Geographic magazine photographers into his mountains at the southern end of Tweedsmuir Park. He talked of that ambition many times, but he had no more idea of how to contact the National Geographic people than how to contact the Queen, and the great photographic mission was never achieved.

What did he do, all these years since the early twenties? He played very hard and he also worked very hard.

In the twenties, thirties, forties, and fifties, decades when ranchers were poor, he founded and built up several ranches. He sold them, commonly, as rapidly as roads reached them. During that time he and Mickey raised a family of five sons and a daughter.

In many ways he was a character of contradictions.

For one thing, he loved company. He would ride twenty miles to find it. He welcomed people on his place casually, but with all sincerity. But he also held a particular feeling about his own ranch and part of that feeling was that it should not be open to visits by people in their family automobiles. A ranch, his place, was something you should reach by saddle horse, perhaps by wagon, occasionally, in good weather, by a robust old high-wheeled truck.

At his last place in the Anahim country the government, doubtless confident that it was doing him a favour, ran a half-decent gravel road beside his western fence line. It only irritated him, and he expressed the wish, as he had done before under different circumstances, that the goddamned government could learn to leave him alone.

His angers, what there were of them, were directed vaguely, against vague entities such as governments, banks, insurance companies, and other grand institutions he only dimly under-stood. But his angers—like his speech, like his manners—were gentle.

He was once asked what he hated most in his life. "Hate?" he said. "Nothing. Nobody. I would never hate anything or any-body. It isn't in me."

So, with the quiet manner that went so oddly with a man naturally flamboyant, with the modesty so oddly set against a man of immense ego, with the capacity for grinding work so oddly matched with a man of princely laziness, he made his way in our world.

Many times he was trail boss on one of the last of North America's long cattle drives, when Anahim Lake's ranchers drove 200 miles east across the Chilcotin plateau to the stock-yards in Williams Lake.

A memory of those days that remains is a photograph of him leaning against a fence at the holding ground that once stood above that town.

He wears a large hat, fearsomely abused, a checked cowboy shirt, immense heavy batwing chaps, and boots with spurs. The ultimate and perfect portrait of the working cowboy.

In truth, Lester was more cowboy than rancher. In truth, he was more frontiersman and mountain man than cowboy.

At the end he was slowed but not hobbled by the heart attacks. In the last year he had started building a new log cabin on his last ranch.

When we last met he said he was planning one more grizzly hunt in the hills to the north of Anahim Lake. "I better do it this year or it might get too late," he said.

He did leave it too late, and missed the last hunt. It can't be said he missed much else in his seventy-eight years.

Would the large crowd that will attend his funeral gratify him? Probably not. He didn't much like funerals. "They give you a bunch of flowers you can't smell any more."

Usually, in that wide and largely empty land, the coffin is brought to the graveyard on the back of a cleaned and polished pickup truck. They brought down Lester's coffin on a horse-drawn wagon. Behind the wagon was led his favourite mare, saddle empty, his old chaps slung on the saddle horse, his 30-06 rifle in the scabbard. No one present could recall ever seeing the horse with the empty saddle at a Chilcotin funeral.